28-DAY
ANTI-INFLAMMATORY
DIET

Easy meal plans, recipes, shopping lists and more to lower inflammation

Prevention

TABLE OF CONTENTS

Breakfast

INTRODUCTION
Wellness Eating that Really Works

What should a person eat to feel their best? Spend 10 minutes Googling or scrolling through social media, and you'll find a dizzying number of answers in the form of fad diets and superfoods. But wellness doesn't have to be the result of complicated or restrictive meal plans—or expensive, inaccessible ingredients or supplements. Far from it, in fact.

As registered dietitians working in joint practice, we've been asked by countless clients for health-supportive eating plans that are simple, balanced, and delicious. And our answer (for more than a decade!) is always the same: anti-inflammatory foods.

Too-high levels of body-wide inflammation are at the core of so many of the chronic health problems we face today. Inflammation contributes to serious diseases like heart disease, diabetes, and cancer. But it can also be the reason a person feels inexplicably fatigued or foggy-headed, why their skin seems so sensitive, or why they're prone to catching every single cold that comes around.

Science shows us that inflammation can stem from many factors. And one of the biggest influences is diet. Choosing the wrong foods too frequently can trigger inflammatory responses in the body that increase the risk for health problems. But picking the right ones can actually fight and prevent inflammation and help us feel our best, both now and in the future. So whether someone is actively seeking to address a chronic health issue or is just looking for a little more pep in their step, shifting to a more anti-inflammatory eating pattern can make a difference.

We've seen the power of anti-inflammatory eating in our practice. Helping clients add more anti-inflammatory foods to their grocery list and implement healthy lifestyle strategies reversed their insulin resistance, put their diabetes into remission, got them off high blood pressure medications, and more. We do this in a way that emphasizes the positive (more health-promoting foods!) rather than focusing on the negative (no dessert!). This leads to positive, sustainable change without feelings of shame, guilt, deprivation, or restriction.

In short? Anti-inflammatory eating has helped our patients thrive. And it can help you too. That' where this plan comes in. Our easy-to-follow 28-day menu is chock-full of delicious meals and snacks designed to turn off your body's inflammatory response, increase your energy, and lower your chronic disease risk. The recipes were developed for two, so you can try this style of eating with a partner or friend (because health journeys are always more fun when you've got support). But if you're going it alone, that's okay too: Leftovers make life easier!

Ready to get started? Great! We're excited to take this journey with you.

Wintana Kiros, RDN, LDN
Jessica "Chef Jess" Swift, MS, RDN

About the Authors

Wintana Kiros, RDN, LDN, is a registered dietitian, health coach, and stylist who helps busy individuals gain their health and confidence back, one healthy habit at a time, at her virtual private practice, Reset Lifestyle. Wintana has been featured in *Shape*, *Parent*, *Martha Stewart*, and *Clean Eating* magazines, as well as *HuffPost* and other publications.

Jessica "Chef Jess" Swift, MS, RDN, is a classically trained chef, registered dietitian, entrepreneur, and innovator with more than 15 years in the healthy food space. She has been featured as a nutrition and culinary expert in *Redbook*; *Elle*; *O, The Oprah Magazine*; Sirius XM's Doctor Radio, Today Show, and Food Network, along with other media outlets.

You can find them working together at ResetLifestyle.com and ChefJess.com.

PART I

ANTI-INFLAMMATORY DIET BASICS

Inflammation is a term that gets tossed around a lot these days. So what exactly is it, and where does it come from? And more importantly, what is it doing to our bodies? Let's begin by taking a quick look at the basics.

What Is Inflammation, Anyway?

Inflammation is the body's response to an irritant—anything from a germ to a toxin to a foreign object (like a splinter). You may have heard that inflammation is bad, and it can be when it goes on for too long. But in brief spurts, inflammation plays a key role in helping your body heal from trauma or illness.

Think about the last time you had a cut or scrape. Once your skin is broken, it becomes flooded with bacteria that can potentially make you sick. The presence of these foreign invaders signals the immune system to launch an attack, triggering the inflammatory process. Fresh blood and nutrients are ferried to the wound, causing it to become red, warm, painful, and swollen. Sure, it's a little uncomfortable. But within a few days the wound has started to heal. A serious infection has been averted, thanks to inflammation!

This type of short-term inflammation is called acute inflammation, and we need it to stay healthy. But problems occur when inflammation is chronic, or ongoing. Inflammation that continues for longer than it should can actually cause damage to healthy tissue, organs and bodily systems. Things get worse when it's left unchecked for long stretches: Over time, chronic inflammation can lead to type 2 diabetes, rheumatoid arthritis, atherosclerosis (the hardening of artery walls from plaque buildup), and cardiovascular disease.

How **CHRONIC INFLAMMATION** Happens

Inflammation can flare up when we sustain an injury or get sick. (That fever or runny nose? These are signs of protective inflammation at work!) But chronic inflammation—the kind that can lead to long-term health problems—is typically driven by your lifestyle. Below are some of the biggest offenders.

DIET

Eating foods that are high in refined carbohydrates or ones that are highly processed (think white bread, cookies, chips, or sugary drinks) on a regular basis can trigger the inflammatory process. The good news? Adding more whole, minimally processed foods to your diet (like fresh fruits and veggies) can have a protective effect.

CHRONIC STRESS

Stress signals the release of hormones like cortisol, which activate the body's fight-or-flight response and turn on inflammatory activity. Developing a daily routine to tame the tension is also another way to combat inflammation. Morning meditation or journaling, anyone?

POOR SLEEP

Consistently logging too few zzz's can also kick the inflammatory process into high gear. What's more, research suggests that women's bodies may be particularly prone to these effects.

SEDENTARY LIFESTYLE

Physical inactivity has been shown to keep the body in a state of low-grade inflammation while regular exercise is tied to reduced levels of inflammatory messengers in the blood.

EXCESS BODY FAT

Fat tissue signals the liver to release inflammatory compo[n] which may be why obesity is tied to higher levels of chronic inflammatio[n] Reaching a healthier weight can ma[ke] a difference by reducing the number inflammatory messengers in the blo[od]

ENVIRONMENTAL TOXINS

Research suggests that chronic exposure to certain chemicals or substances, including endocrine disruptors such as bisphenol-A (or BPA, found in some plastics), may contribute to heightened levels of inflammation.

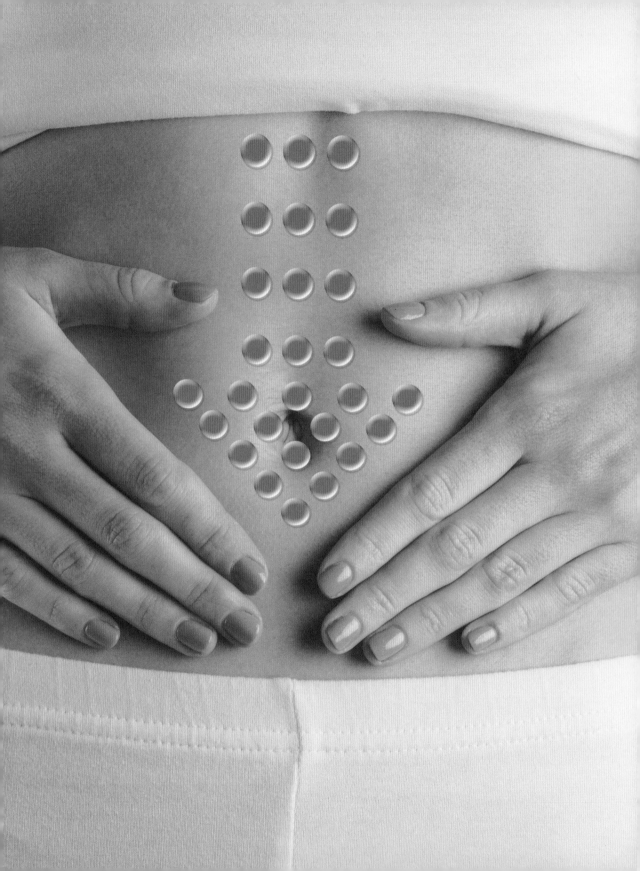

The Body on Chronic Inflammation

Constantly being in inflammation mode can wreak havoc on the body, though early on, the signs can be pretty vague. In some cases excess inflammation might leave you feeling tired or foggy-headed. You might notice that you're frequently plagued by digestive problems, skin rashes, or muscle aches. Or perhaps you feel like you catch colds all the time and they take forever to go away. These can all be warning signs that your inflammation levels are higher than they should be.

What's more, the alarm bells of chronic inflammation tend to chime louder with time. The longer the body stays in a high-inflammation state, the bigger—and more obvious—the toll can become. That's because the effects of inflammation are cumulative. The damages caused over years or decades may eventually lead to serious health issues that can affect your quality of life as well as your longevity. There's good news, though: Because inflammation's effects are slow to add up, there's almost always a chance to halt them in their tracks—or even reverse them.

5 Pillars of the ANTI-INFLAMMATORY Diet

If you're feeling a bit unsettled right now, we get it. Chronic inflammation is a big deal, and thinking about all of the contributing factors (stressful work projects! late-night Netflix binges! afternoon candy breaks!) can be overwhelming. It might seem like getting the whole situation in check would require a total life overhaul.

But here's the truth: You don't have to tackle everything at once. Improving your health can feel a whole lot more manageable when you focus on one thing at a time. So let's turn our attention to everyone's favorite topic: food! Believe it or not, simply eating more wholesome, minimally processed foods (and fewer of their highly processed, less-nutritious counterparts) can cause chronic inflammation to take a significant nosedive. In fact, enjoying a varied diet rich in anti-inflammatory foods and low in pro-inflammatory foods has been shown to reduce markers of inflammation in the blood by as much as 20%.

As for which foods will give you the most inflammation-fighting bang for your buck? Rather than focus on individual menu items, let's start by looking at the major properties that anti-inflammatory foods have—and the sources in which they tend to be the most abundant.

HIGH IN FIBER

When it comes to fighting inflammation, fiber-rich foods are truly our best friends. Fiber stabilizes blood sugar, preventing blood sugar spikes that cause the body to overproduce harmful free radical molecules and release inflammatory messengers. Fiber also keeps you satisfied for hours, lowers cholesterol, aids in the removal of toxins from the body, supports immune health, and helps you stay regular.

Despite these impressive benefits, only 7% of us are meeting our daily fiber quota. (For those under 50, that's 25 g a day for women and 38 g a day for men, according to the National Academy of Medicine. For those 50 and over, it's 21 g a day for women and 30 g a day for men.) In other words, the majority of us can make a dent in our inflammation levels simply by getting more fiber!

SOLUBLE FIBER

This type of fiber attracts water to form a gel-like substance in the gut. Because soluble fiber isn't easily absorbed into the bloodstream, it effectively lowers blood sugar, increasing satiety and keeping cravings at bay. Soluble fiber can also lower your risk for heart disease.

FIND IT IN:

Beans, avocado, sweet potato, pears, figs, oats, barley, carrots.

INSOLUBLE FIBER

This type does not absorb water. Rather, it works like an intestinal broom, giving it a clean sweep to move stool and toxins through your gut to support healthy bowel movements and prevent constipation.

FIND IT IN:

Prunes, leafy greens, whole wheat, nuts, and unpeeled apples.

SHOULD I TAKE A FIBER SUPPLEMENT?

We're fans of meeting your daily fiber needs through food whenever possible. Fiber-rich foods come packaged with other key nutrients (like vitamins and minerals) that you won't get from a powder or pill. That said, a supplement may be helpful if you struggle to get enough fiber from diet alone. Talk about the pros and cons with your healthcare provider before starting a fiber supplement regimen.

OMEGA-3-RICH

Omega-3 fatty acids get a lot of love these days, and for good reason. These polyunsaturated fats are vital to building and maintaining the structure of our cell walls and they play an integral role in heart, lung, blood vessel, and immune system function. To top it all off, omega-3s inhibit the secretion of harmful compounds that trigger inflammation. You want them on your plate!

Omega-3s are considered essential, meaning you have to get them from dietary sources (the body doesn't make them). Women should aim to get 1.1 g per day, while men should get 1.6 g. A three-ounce serving of wild-caught salmon will get you there.

FIND THEM IN:

Fatty fish such as salmon, tuna, mackerel, and herring; other sources include oysters, chia seeds, walnuts, flaxseeds, and hemp seeds.

PACKED WITH POLYPHENOLS

Found in colorful plant foods, polyphenols are micronutrients that act as powerful antioxidants with the capacity to prevent or reverse inflammatory damage caused by free radicals—the unstable atoms that can harm cells. Many experts regard polyphenols as "lifespan essentials" for their potential to reduce chronic disease risk. Put simply, polyphenols help turn off the body's inflammation switch.

One of the best ways to fill up on polyphenols is by eating plenty of fresh produce, especially brightly colored choices such as leafy greens, citrus fruits, berries, grapes, carrots, sweet potatoes, and bell peppers. Make it a goal to get as many hues on your plate as you can each day—different colors are signs that different fruits and veggies pack their own unique antioxidants. You'll get anthocyanins, known to support heart health, from blueberries or red cabbage, and lycopene, found in tomatoes, offers protection from the sun's UV rays and may reduce the risk for some cancers.

Fruits and veggies aren't the only sources of polyphenols, though. Many herbs and spices are teeming with antioxidant power, especially cinnamon, curry, dill, oregano, ginger, and rosemary. Teas, including green, black, white, and oolong, are polyphenol-rich too. That gives you even more reason to add a shake of cinnamon to your morning oatmeal or sit down for an afternoon tea break.

FIND THEM IN:

Berries, leafy greens, tomatoes, beets, red cabbage, sweet potatoes, beans, dark chocolate, herbs and spices, tea, and coffee.

LOW IN REFINED CARBS

This probably isn't the first time you've seen or heard a recommendation to reduce your intake of refined or highly processed carbohydrates like white bread, white pasta, baked goods, and added sugars. So what is it about these foods, when consumed regularly, that can be so problematic?

To understand the relationship between refined carbohydrates and inflammation, let's imagine the body as a furnace. Foods high in refined carbohydrates are a source of fuel for the furnace, but they get burned up quickly, like paper, as opposed to slowly and steadily, like a log. This fast and furious fuel hit causes the body's blood sugar levels to spike and crash, resulting in an instant burst of energy followed by a slump. As your energy levels fall (and your appetite rears back up), you find yourself craving more refined carbs to bring your blood sugar levels back up.

This cycle of spike-and-crash doesn't just mess with your energy levels. Blood sugar spikes send the body's production of free radical molecules into overdrive, signaling the release of a flurry of inflammatory messengers. Over time, this can contribute to higher levels of chronic inflammation and the serious health effects that come with it.

FIND THEM IN:

White flour, white bread, white rice, white pasta, pastries and baked goods, sweetened beverages, breakfast cereals, table sugar, high fructose corn syrup, and agave syrup.

PROTEIN POWERED

While foods high in refined carbohydrates cause blood sugar spikes that trigger inflammation, foods and meals that are high in lean protein (as well as our friends fiber and healthy fats) do the opposite. Protein-focused meals serve to keep blood sugar levels stable, preventing the release of excess insulin and thwarting the formation of inflammatory free radicals. They'll help you feel better too, since you'll stay satisfied and energized for longer. No need to scrounge for a snack an hour after lunch, thank you very much!

So how much protein is enough? We recommend that our clients get 25 to 30 g at each meal, depending on their calorie needs. (Half a cup of Greek yogurt with nuts and berries or three to four ounces of chicken breast on top of a green salad should do the trick.) Getting enough protein at breakfast is particularly important: It sets the tone for stable blood sugar levels and reduces the risk of inflammation-causing carb crashes throughout the day. So add some low-fat milk and peanut butter to that bowl of oatmeal or grab a hard-boiled egg with that granola bar. Later on, you'll be glad you did!

TIME TO EAT!

Is it better to eat three squares a day or have more frequent mini-meals? When it comes to keeping inflammation at bay, smaller meals eaten more often— think four to five per day— have the edge. We teach our clients the importance of eating a protein-forward meal within one hour of waking to help stabilize their blood sugar and to nourish their bodies every three to four hours after that. Keeping those blood sugar levels nice and steady minimizes the spikes that can trigger inflammation. Plus, you'll never get so hungry that you end up scarfing down an entire sleeve of cookies.

Worried that eating so often means that you'll have to be thinking about food (or actively prepping it) all day long? We hear you. Our 28-day meal plan is designed to keep you fueled while maximizing convenience, so you don't have to deal with being in the kitchen 24/7.

FIND THEM IN:

Seafood, poultry, eggs, low-fat dairy, beans, nuts, tofu, and tempeh.

Why Is This the Best "Diet"?

"Diet" can definitely feel like a four-letter word, especially when you're thinking in terms of highly restrictive or hard-to-follow eating plans designed for speedy weight loss. (We're looking at you, keto diet!) An anti-inflammatory diet does not fit into that category. In fact, we prefer to think of it as a set of healthy, sustainable eating habits rather than a diet.

Our eating plan serves up specific meal ideas to help you get the hang of eating anti-inflammatory-style (and you can certainly repeat the recipes after you've reached the end!). But after that, you can take what you've learned and put that knowledge toward making healthy eating choices that work for you. If that sounds a lot more doable than complicated meal plans, we wholeheartedly agree!

There's plenty more that sets our eating plan apart from other diets. An anti-inflammatory eating style:

Is evidence based

Decades' worth of research has shown that many whole, minimally processed foods have anti-inflammatory properties that can support health. And when eaten regularly, these foods can lead to a reduced risk for chronic diseases.

Adds instead of restricts

Anti-inflammatory eating simply means including foods in your diet that reduce inflammation. When you do that, there will naturally be less room for foods that do the opposite.

Aims to improve health, not help with weight loss

The goal of anti-inflammatory eating is to choose foods that will nourish and protect your body. If the scale happens to nudge downward—and very well may—that's great too! You may find that you shed some weight because you're filling your plate with more whole foods and eating fewer of the processed kind. But it's not the end-all, be-all.

Includes fun foods

Even pro-inflammatory foods like chocolate chip cookies or pizza don't have to be entirely off-limits. You can enjoy the occasional candy bar or bakery muffin as long as you pair it with healthy fat, protein, and fiber to minimize the effects on your blood sugar.

Fits your lifestyle and honors your food culture and traditions

You can choose anti-inflammatory foods at restaurants or dinner parties. You can tweak family recipes to include more inflammation-fighting ingredients. In short, you don't have to change your life to eat this way. For tips and ideas on how to do that, see page 24.

Can be done for life

Sure, most of us could go without carbs or sugar for a few days. But at some point a dinner party, or a holiday, or a vacation will come up—or you just get sick of feeling deprived. Because anti-inflammatory eating is easy and flexible, you can stick with it for the long haul.

The Best (And Worst) ANTI-INFLAMMATORY Foods

We've talked about how some foods have the power to prevent or thwart the inflammatory process and keep body-wide inflammation low, while others tend to open the floodgates for inflammatory markers and increase the risk for chronic inflammation. Here are some of the menu mainstays we regularly recommend to our clients, along with the foods that we recommend eating less of.

Inflammation Fighters: Eat Up!

UNSATURATED OILS AND SEEDS

We're big fans of oils, including olive, avocado, and flaxseed, as well as seeds like flax, sesame, and pumpkin. They're rich in healthy fats (including monounsaturated fatty acids and omega-3s), which inhibit pro-inflammatory enzymes.

VEGETABLES

Carrots, kale, tomato, cabbage, bell peppers, Brussels sprouts, bok choy, cauliflower, and broccoli are some of our favorite polyphenol-rich picks. They pack a big antioxidant punch to protect cells from free radical damage.

FRUITS

Berries, apples, citrus, cherries, and pomegranates are polyphenol-packed. They also serve up fiber to help the body efficiently remove toxins and support immune health by feeding good bacteria in the gut.

WHOLE GRAINS

Pick whole-wheat bread or pasta, brown rice, quinoa, barley, or oatmeal over refined grains whenever possible. Whole-grain foods are fiber-rich, so they won't spike your blood sugar. And since they haven't been stripped of their nutrients, they offer key vitamins and minerals that you won't get from refined carbs.

TEA AND COFFEE

These sippers are rich in antioxidants that may protect against cellular damage. Just limit the extras like added sugar or high-fat creamers.

WATER

Plain old H_2O helps you stay hydrated, allowing the body to effectively flush out toxins.

SUPPLEMENTS

Spirulina, curcumin, bromelain, vitamin D, and fish oils can all reduce inflammation. These supplements provide a powerhouse of antioxidant properties, reducing inflammatory markers in the body and protecting cells from oxidative stress.

LEAN PROTEIN

Lean poultry, fatty fish, low-fat dairy, eggs, beans, and soy foods like tofu and tempeh support stable blood sugar levels and keep you fuller longer. Fatty fish like salmon, mackerel, tuna, herring, and sardines have the added benefit of omega-3s. You'll get an extra helping of phytonutrients from plant proteins like beans or soy too.

HERBS, SPICES, AND CONDIMENTS

Flavor enhancers such as black pepper, rosemary, turmeric, ginger, saffron, cinnamon, and garlic are rich in inflammation-fighting polyphenols. That's also true for condiments like fiery harissa paste or herb-infused chimichurri sauce or pesto—the olive oil base delivers a dose of healthy fats.

ARE SUPPLEMENTS WORTH IT?

The supplement aisle is filled with powders and pills that claim to reduce inflammation and lower your risk for chronic diseases. But are they actually effective? The answer is...maybe. Options for supplementation include spirulina, curcumin, bromelain, vitamin D, and fish oil, which all boast antioxidant properties that may reduce inflammatory markers in the body and protect cells from inflammatory stress. That said, researchers are still learning how supplements may impact the body and the dosage amounts that may be most effective. What's more, supplements aren't a substitute for a healthy diet, and they could interact with certain medications you may be taking. If you're thinking about starting a supplement, check with your doctor first.

Inflammation Triggers: Be Mindful

FOODS RICH IN SATURATED FATS

Fatty meats, full-fat dairy, baked goods, fried food, and packaged snacks tend to be high in saturated fats, which raise LDL ("bad") cholesterol and triglycerides while lowering HDL ("good") cholesterol. Over time, this can increase the risk for a heart attack or stroke.

REFINED CARBOHYDRATES

We're talking white rice, white bread, white pasta, baked goods, and added sugars (including table sugar, honey, and maple syrup). Refined carbs are broken down quickly by the body, triggering a rapid blood sugar spike that increases inflammation.

PROCESSED MEATS

In addition to being high in saturated fat, foods like bacon, sausage, cold cuts, and charcuterie contain preservatives such as nitrates, which can raise levels of inflammation and may contribute to an increased risk for cancer.

CHARRED MEATS

High-heat cooking methods like frying, smoking, or grilling can cause animal proteins (including meat, poultry, and seafood) to develop carcinogenic compounds such as polycyclic aromatic hydrocarbons (PAHs) and heterocyclic amines (HCAs). These compounds are tied to an increased risk of cancers, including colon, breast, and prostate cancers.

TRANS FATS

We said that no foods are off-limits on an anti-inflammatory diet, but the truth is, there is one important exception. Trans fats, also called partially hydrogenated oils, are fats that have been chemically altered to stay solid at room temperature. They're often added to packaged or processed foods like margarine, fried foods, baked goods, coffee creamer, microwave popcorn, potato chips, and store-bought baked goods. Trans fats significantly raise inflammation and increase the risk for heart disease, and experts agree that it's best to steer clear of these as much as possible.

SWEETENED BEVERAGES

Soft drinks, juices, hot chocolate, and coffee drinks loaded with syrup and whipped cream are high in added sugar (and offer little, if any, nutrition). They can ramp up inflammation—and consumption of these treats has been tied to obesity and elevated levels of LDL cholesterol.

Finding Your Balance

Anti-inflammatory foods are delicious and satisfying. But...there's a good chance that at least a few of your favorites fall on that *other* list. So how can you incorporate some of those pro-inflammatory foods (which, yes, taste really good!) into your diet without negatively impacting your health?

We're big believers in the 80/20 rule: Eighty percent of the time, your eating pattern should be based around foods that have anti-inflammatory properties; for the other 20%, your diet can consist of fun foods that may promote inflammation. This is the concept we teach our clients who are not actively managing chronic disease and simply want to eat in a way that supports a healthy, well-balanced lifestyle. All-or-nothing food mindsets are hard to stick with! So instead of saying, "I can't eat that," you can say, "I can eat part

of it today and have some leftovers tomorrow." Sounds a lot more doable, right?

Following the 80/20 rule gives you some wiggle room to enjoy treats every day, like a serving of chips with your lunch or a small bowl of ice cream after dinner. In fact, we encourage a daily splurge! Allowing yourself to enjoy fun foods on a regular basis helps you avoid that diet-y, deprivation mindset. We also find that daily treats tend to be more enjoyable than eating "good" all week to save up for a weekend treat spree, which often leads to overeating (and feeling crummy on Monday morning).

Keep in mind, also, that it's often possible to reduce or diminish a treat's inflammatory effects by making sure all of your meals or snacks incorporate protein, fat, and fiber. (We like to call this the

CHEAT FOODS, BEGONE

Learning how to fit fun foods into your lifestyle is more sustainable than constantly fighting the urge to eat them. Let's retire the concept of cheat foods. Sticking with the 80/20 rule means splurging on your favorite foods in moderation without shame or guilt. You're enjoying yourself— not cheating!

PFF Principle. For more advice on making this work, see page 27.) This will help stave off inflammatory blood sugar spikes—plus you'll fill up faster and stay satisfied longer, which can reduce the urge to overdo it on your fun food or come back for another snack an hour later. Ordering white pasta at a restaurant? Pick the entree that also includes chicken or shrimp and have it with a side salad. Enjoying a cinnamon scone for breakfast on Saturday morning? Add a side of scrambled eggs and some fresh fruit. You get the idea!

This 28-day plan is designed to be a little stricter than our usual 80/20 approach to help you get into an anti-inflammatory eating groove (though there's still room for some fun foods and treats). Once you've developed that healthy-eating foundation, you can start adding in daily treats using the PFF Principle.

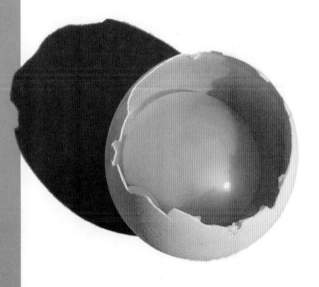

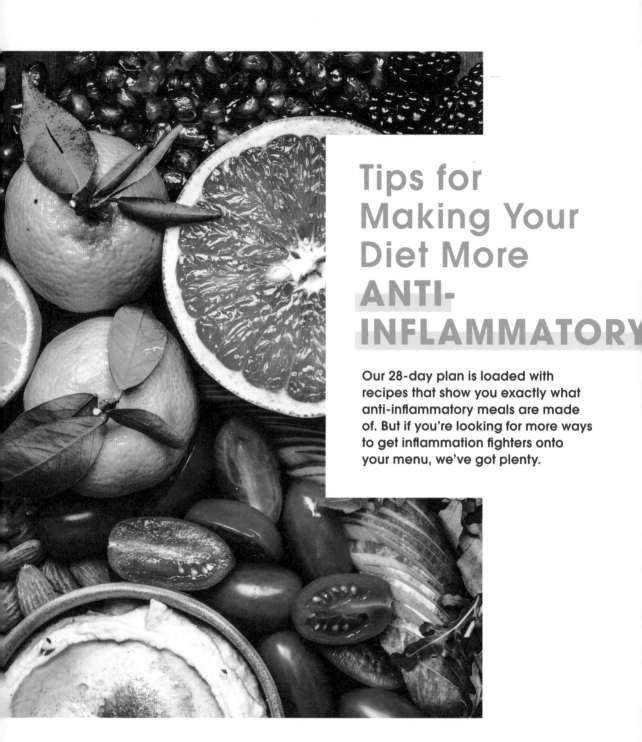

Tips for Making Your Diet More ANTI-INFLAMMATORY

Our 28-day plan is loaded with recipes that show you exactly what anti-inflammatory meals are made of. But if you're looking for more ways to get inflammation fighters onto your menu, we've got plenty.

13 Ways to Get More Anti-Inflammatory Foods

- [ ] Use whole-wheat bread or tortillas in sandwiches or wraps.

- [ ] Cook with olive oil instead of butter.

- [ ] Top breakfast cereal or oatmeal with fresh berries.

- [ ] Sprinkle yogurt or a parfait with chia seeds.

- [ ] Sweeten baked goods with mashed bananas or pureed dates in lieu of some (or all) of the sugar.

- [ ] Use unsweetened applesauce in place of oil in baked goods.

- [ ] Add a handful of chopped kale or baby spinach to soups or sauces during the last few minutes of cooking.

- [ ] Snack on walnuts or almonds.

- [ ] Swap the mayo in sandwiches for hummus or white bean spread.

- [ ] Choose frozen grapes instead of candy.

- [ ] Swap some of the ground meat in lasagna or taco filling for chopped mushrooms.

- [ ] Finish food prep with a grinding of black pepper.

- [ ] Toss a handful of greens and a spoonful of ground flaxseeds into a smoothie.

Anti-Inflammatory Food Swaps

Sometimes changing up a few ingredients is all it takes to give a meal more inflammation-fighting power.

INSTEAD OF	TRY
White rice	Brown rice, quinoa, or bulgur wheat
White pasta	Whole-wheat pasta or quinoa pasta
Instant mashed potatoes	Mashed sweet potatoes
Candy bar	Dark chocolate with almonds
Hamburger	Black bean burger
Canned fruit in syrup	Fresh fruit
White bread	Whole-wheat bread
French fries	Baked sweet potato fries
Lunch meat	Canned tuna in water or olive oil
Pepperoni pizza	Veggie pizza on whole-wheat crust

If you find that some of these swaps just aren't a substitute for the real thing, that's okay! After all, it's not quite the same having your grandma's cheesy rice casserole without the rice, right? Luckily, with our PFF Principle, you can still enjoy the foods that mean the most to you without undoing your anti-inflammatory lifestyle.

The PFF Principle

Pairing fun foods with PFF—that's protein, healthy fats, and fiber—will keep your blood sugar stable, and in turn, keep inflammation in check. In practice, that might look like one of these combos.

ALONG WITH	TRY
White pasta	Turkey meatballs (protein) and garlicky sautéed spinach (fiber)
Hamburger on white bun	Oven-baked sweet potato fries or a green salad (fiber)
Canned fruit in syrup	Plain Greek yogurt or cottage cheese (protein); rinse the fruit before eating to remove some of the sugary syrup
Chocolate chip cookie	Low-fat milk (protein) and a handful of nuts (fiber and healthy fat)
French fries	Grilled chicken breast (protein) and side of salad (fiber)
Lunch meat	Pair with whole-grain bread (fiber), avocado (healthy fat)
Ice cream	Fresh berries (fiber)
Steak	Baked potato with skin and sautéed green beans (fiber); limit red meat to twice a month

PART 2

HOW TO USE THIS PLAN

Our 28-day plan is designed for people without chronic diseases who are looking for a delicious, sustainable eating pattern to reduce or prevent inflammation. Rather than offer a quick-fix program for dropping, say, two jeans sizes in four weeks, we're here to get you into the habit of eating anti-inflammatory foods that help you feel your best now and support your health long-term.

Put another way, this plan is an opportunity to learn how to eat meals that are going to keep you satisfied, decrease sugar cravings, and generally help you feel your best. Once you've reached the end, you can apply those same principles to making your own anti-inflammatory food choices—for life.

Let's Get Started

O ur 28-day plan is divided into four weeks. Each week features anti-inflammatory recipes for breakfasts, lunches, dinners, and a handful of snacks and desserts. Each day features three meals plus two snacks (or one snack and one dessert). We encourage you to try everything and repeat a few favorites!

The meals, snacks, and treats in our plan are centered around core nutrition principles proven to help decrease inflammation. You can continue to use them even after you've completed the 28-day plan. We suggest you:

- Have a protein-forward breakfast (15 to 30 g protein) to stabilize your blood sugar in the morning and reduce midday cravings.

- Eat every 3 to 5 hours to keep your blood sugar stable.

- Include 8 to 10 g fiber at each meal to increase satiety, support gut health, and remove excess cholesterol and toxins from your body.

- Eat at least two servings of fish per week to boost omega-3 consumption.

- Follow the 80/20 rule so you don't feel deprived. That means choosing nourishing, anti-inflammatory foods at most meals and snacks, while also allowing yourself to enjoy inflammatory foods in small servings most days. Remember to pair foods from this category, which may include refined carbohydrates, with protein, fat, and fiber (PFF) to support steady blood sugar, which prevents excess inflammation.

As you move through the plan, consider how you can begin to incorporate other anti-inflammatory habits into your day. Drink plenty of water, make time for physical activity, and try to get enough sleep. If you're struggling in the stress management department, consider strategies that could help you tame the tension and regain a sense of calm.

The Truth About Calories

Most eating plans spend a lot of time focused on calories. But this one? Not so much. Caloric needs can vary based on age, body size, physical activity, and other factors, so we shied away from a one-size-fits-all approach in favor of offering flexibility. By following this plan as is, you'll consume between 1,500 and 1,800 calories per day. If you're highly active and find that you need more fuel to sustain you, make adjustments as needed (like doubling the snacks, for instance).

And if you want to take in fewer calories, you can cut out a snack or dessert, but we encourage you to calculate your individual calorie needs before making any changes. (We recommend clients use the Mayo Clinic's online calorie calculator.) While many quick-fix weight-loss plans clock in at 1,200 calories per day or less, most people need more than that to feel satisfied. Twelve hundred calories also makes it difficult to embrace the 80/20 rule, since it leaves very little room for fun foods. It's a hard number to work with over the long term.

Get the Most Out of the Next 28 Days

In addition to a grocery list, meal plan, and recipes, each day you will be provided with a wellness tracker that you'll fill in. This will help you keep tabs on that day's meal plan and also give you an opportunity to home in on factors that may impact your ability to stick to the plan, including hydration, movement, sleep, and mood.

This type of tracking is shown to help people reach their health goals because it increases awareness, which in turn prompts change. When you see in black and white how much, how little, or how inconsistently you drink water, move, and sleep, you become more cognizant of which areas need more attention. Then you can create goals and actionable steps outlining exactly how you're going to achieve those objectives.

On the next pages, we explain the four things you'll be tracking.

1. HYDRATION

Why: Proper hydration is necessary for good sleep, energy, mental clarity, and bowel function. It's especially important in this plan because you'll be eating plenty of high-fiber dishes, which—without proper hydration—can lead to constipation. While individual needs vary based on activity level, the climate you live in, and other factors, a good goal to aim for is eight 8-ounce glasses a day.

WHAT YOU'LL RECORD

- How many glasses of water you drink each day

KEY THINGS TO KNOW

- A quick way to determine if you are dehydrated is to look at your urine. If it is pale and clear, you are well hydrated. However, if it is a dark yellow, it's time to drink more H_2O.

- Caffeinated beverages act as diuretics. All the more reason to sip water throughout the day if you're a coffee lover.

DRINK UP!

- Buy a reusable water bottle and carry it everywhere.

- Keep a big jug filled in your fridge for cold water that's ready to go.

- Jazz up your water with fresh mint or basil leaves, a squeeze of fresh lemon or lime, mashed berries, or cucumber slices.

- Carry your wellness tracker with you at all times. This may be enough to prompt you to drink more.

2. MOVEMENT

Why: Just like food, movement is also very medicinal, especially as it pertains to inflammation. Because regular exercise is tied to reduced levels of inflammatory messengers in the blood, it's helpful to stay on top of how much you're getting.

WHAT YOU'LL RECORD

- What type of movement or workout you engaged in

- How long you exercised

- At what intensity you exercised

KEY THINGS TO KNOW

- Always consult your physician prior to starting an exercise program.

- Listen to your body. Stop right away if you experience: pain or discomfort in your chest, neck, jaw, upper back, or one or both arms; shortness of breath; nausea/vomiting; lightheadedness; dizziness; or irregular heartbeat. Inform your doctor right away if symptoms resolve with rest. If they do not, call 911.

- Muscle fatigue and mild soreness are normal. Pain and discomfort are not. Again, listen to your body.

MOVE MORE!

- If exercise is new for you or you haven't exercised in a while, start slow and keep workouts short, gradually adding more time. Doing too much too soon can result not only in pain and fatigue, it can also squash motivation.

- Track your steps with a step counter or fitness app, wearable fitness tracker, or pedometer. Aim to add 250 to 500 more steps every week until you reach an ideal long-term goal of 7,500 steps or more each day.

- Commit to doing more chores and daily tasks manually, whether it be washing the dishes by hand, walking to the mailbox, or taking the stairs instead of the elevator. Remember, every single time you move, it counts toward better health.

3. SLEEP

Why: Consistent lack of shut-eye can lead to inflammation. Inadequate rest can also elevate blood pressure, blood sugars, and cravings and also contribute to weight gain, irritability, and even risk of dementia. Get your recommended seven to eight hours a night, though, and you can enjoy all the anti-inflammatory, antioxidant, and healing health benefits that come with this daily reboot.

WHAT YOU'LL RECORD

- What time you went to bed
- What time you woke up
- How well you slept

KEY THINGS TO KNOW

- Both quantity and quality matter. If you are having a hard time falling asleep or staying asleep, evaluate your sleep hygiene, the healthy habits that contribute to a good night's sleep.
- If you're practicing good sleep hygiene and still have issues, talk to your doctor.

SLEEP SOUNDLY!

- Avoid food, alcohol, and sodium before bed, and caffeine after 2 p.m.
- Stick with a consistent sleep schedule. Go to sleep and wake up around the same time every day, even on weekends.
- Get outside. Exposure to sunshine during the day lowers daytime melatonin, while a dark environment during the night raises melatonin levels. This hormone plays an important role in promoting sleep.
- Avoid screens at least 30 minutes before bedtime. The blue light is especially alerting for the brain.

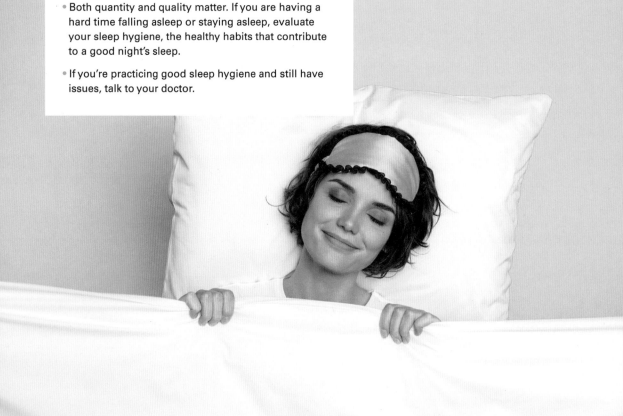

4. MOOD

Why: We all have days when we wake up on the wrong side of the bed. However, when a poor mood is a result of stress, worry, anxiety, or depression, it's time to take action. Your body and mind are intimately linked. Negative feelings can increase stress hormones, raise heart rate, and elevate blood pressure. Of course, many different factors can be at play when it comes to these emotions. Tracking your mood throughout this program can help you gain some valuable insight as to how your food and water intake, movement, and sleep affect your feelings.

WHAT YOU'LL RECORD

• Your overall mood for that day

WHAT TO WATCH FOR

• If your mood is consistently poor even if you've met all of your needs (quality sleep, regular social activities, accepting and receiving emotional support, daily movement, healthy diet), talk with your doctor. It is OK to not be OK. It's also OK to seek additional support; that is what professionals like therapists are here for.

TAKE CARE OF YOURSELF!

• **Be aware of and tend to your needs, including:** basics such as food, water, shelter, clothing, and sleep; strong and supportive relationships; respect and self-esteem; sense of purpose in life; and personal safety, security, and good health.

• Stick to the simple things. Sunshine, nature, a time-out from social media, quiet time to yourself, and saying no can make all the difference in the world when it comes to your emotions and coping skills.

FAQs

More ways to ensure this plan works for you.

Q: How do I know the plan is working?

A: There's a good chance you'll start to notice some positive changes like more energy and fewer cravings within days or weeks. That said, the benefits of anti-inflammatory eating are cumulative: The more you do it, the more likely you'll be to enjoy optimal health and reduce your chronic disease risk long-term.

Q: I don't have tons of time to meal-prep. Will this plan work for me?

A: Yes! The recipes in this plan are simple and straightforward, so you won't spend hours in the kitchen every day. Many are also designed to yield leftovers to lighten your cooking load. You'll also find weekly shopping lists, so mapping out your market trip won't feel like a major event.

Q: I'm on a budget. Will this plan work for me?

A: Yes again! We know that buying tons of new ingredients every week can add up, so we designed many of our meals to include ingredients that overlap. It's a simple strategy that helps keep grocery costs in check while reducing food waste at the same time.

How to Store Leftovers

Most leftovers can be refrigerated in airtight containers for two to five days, depending what they are. But there are few things you can do to make them last longer and taste better the second time around.

Store Separately

Meats and vegetables not only reheat at different rates, but you also may want to use them for different meals in upcoming days. Storing them separately helps maintain optimal freshness and gives you additional meal-planning flexibility.

Keep It Whole

If you cook steak, pork, or chicken and the recipe calls for slicing it, but you know you are not going to eat it all, it is better to keep it whole. It is less likely to dry out, especially if you plan on reheating it.

Wait to Dress and Top

Instead of tossing or topping with vinaigrettes, tender herbs and greens, or crunchy nuts, leave these garnishes out and store separately. Drizzle, fold in, sprinkle, and add just before serving.

Q: Can I make substitutions if I don't like something?

A: Sure thing! Just try to stick to similar foods within the same family. If you're not a fan of quinoa, for instance, try brown rice or millet. You can also swap out fruits (like blueberries for raspberries), non-starchy veggies (like broccoli for bok choy), beans (like chickpeas for black beans), and nuts or seeds (like cashews for walnuts), no problem. Virtually all plant foods offer anti-inflammatory benefits, so they're always a win.

If you need to change up an animal protein, just make sure you're substituting one lean meat for another. For example, you can use boneless, skinless chicken breast in place of lean pork tenderloin, but don't replace it with a steak. We encourage you to stick with fatty fish like salmon, simply because there aren't many alternatives that are as rich in omega-3s.

Q: What should I do after the plan is over?

A: Keep up the good work! You can continue to enjoy some (or all!) of the recipes from the plan while using what you've learned about anti-inflammatory eating to keep making healthy choices. And if you're not quite ready to strike out on your own yet, no worries. You can always do the plan again, or come back to it later on if you feel like you need a refresher.

Q: I messed up. What should I do?

A: Overdoing it with a treat or falling off the plan for a day or two isn't the end of the world. Nobody's perfect! Give yourself grace and pick up right where you left off. Getting back on track will make you feel good.

Q: Any final words of advice for helping me succeed?

A: Change can be tough, especially if an anti-inflammatory eating style is vastly different from how you typically eat. So keep your why (better health!) in mind and remember that you've got the power to make real, positive change. We've seen it happen with countless clients, and we know you can do it, too.

PART 3

THE MEAL PLAN

PANTRY STAPLES

Be sure to always have these essentials on hand throughout the meal plan.

- √ all-purpose flour
- √ apple cider vinegar
- √ baking powder
- √ baking soda
- √ balsamic vinegar
- √ black pepper
- √ canola oil
- √ chili powder
- √ crushed red pepper flakes
- √ dried oregano

- √ Dutch process cocoa
- √ extra virgin olive oil
- √ garlic powder
- √ grated nutmeg
- √ ground cayenne
- √ ground cinnamon
- √ ground coriander
- √ ground cumin
- √ ground sumac
- √ ground sweet paprika

- √ honey
- √ kosher salt
- √ nonstick cooking spray
- √ pure vanilla extract
- √ red wine vinegar
- √ white wine vinegar

DAY 1

BREAKFAST
No-Syrup Pancakes + ½ cup small curd cottage cheese

SNACK
Stress-Less Smoothie

LUNCH
Chopped Egg Salad Toast

SNACK
1 apple with 2 Tbsp peanut butter

DINNER
Chili with Wheat Berries and Beans

DAY 2

BREAKFAST
Mango-Coconut Chia Pudding

SNACK
Berry, Chia, and Mint Smoothie

LUNCH
◎ Chili with Wheat Berries and Beans

SNACK
Snow Pea and Ricotta Toasts

DINNER
Striped Bass with Radish Salsa Verde

DESSERT
Coconut Truffle

DAY 3

BREAKFAST
2 Spinach and Goat Cheese Egg Muffins + 6 oz Greek yogurt with ½ cup raspberries

SNACK
Stress-Less Smoothie

LUNCH
Salmon Salad with Green Goddess Dressing

SNACK
1 hard-boiled egg on whole-wheat bread

DINNER
Herb-Pounded Chicken with Arugula

DAY 4

BREAKFAST
◎ No-Syrup Pancakes + ½ cup small curd cottage cheese

SNACK
Stress-Less Smoothie

LUNCH
Turkey and Greens Soup + 1 cup brown rice

DINNER
◎ Striped Bass with Radish Salsa Verde

DAY 5

BREAKFAST
◎ 2 Spinach and Goat Cheese Egg Muffins + 6 oz Greek yogurt with ½ cup raspberries

SNACK
1 cup edamame

LUNCH
◎ Salmon Salad with Green Goddess Dressing

SNACK
1 cup sliced cucumber with 4 Tbsp hummus

DINNER
Slow Cooker Pork Pozole Verde + 1 small whole-wheat roll

DAY 6

BREAKFAST
◎ Mango-Coconut Chia Pudding + 2 Tbsp peanut butter on whole-wheat bread

SNACK
◎ Snow Pea and Ricotta Toasts

LUNCH
◎ Turkey and Greens Soup + 1 cup brown rice

DINNER
Seared Salmon with Roasted Cauliflower + 1 cup quinoa

DESSERT
Roasted Apples with Greek Yogurt

DAY 7

BREAKFAST
◎ 2 Spinach and Goat Cheese Egg Muffins + 6 oz Greek yogurt with ½ cup raspberries

SNACK
Stress-Less Smoothie

LUNCH
◎ Seared Salmon with Roasted Cauliflower + 1 cup quinoa

SNACK
1 cup sliced cucumber with 4 Tbsp hummus

DINNER
◎ Slow Cooker Pork Pozole Verde + 1 small whole-wheat roll

DESSERT
◎ Coconut Truffle

WEEK 1

Below are exact amounts of everything you will need for Week 1. Remember: These lists are for two people. If you're doing the plan by yourself, simply cut the measurements in half.

Shopping List

PRODUCE

5 apples

2 cups arugula

1 avocado (plus more for serving)

1 5-oz pkg. baby spinach

1 medium beet

1 large head cauliflower

12 oz cherry tomatoes

¼ cup chives

1 cup cilantro

2 cucumbers

5 Tbsp dill

2 cups edamame

1¾ cups flat-leaf parsley

11 cloves garlic

8 oz green beans

2 cups kale

3 lemons

2 limes

1 mango

⅓ cup mint leaves

1 5-oz pkg. mixed greens

2 onions

8 peaches

2 large poblano peppers

1 bunch radishes (plus more for serving)

7½ cups raspberries

1 large red bell pepper

1 red onion

4 tsp rosemary

2 scallions

1 lb small new potatoes

4 oz snow peas

2 cups strawberries

1 tsp tarragon leaves

1 bunch thyme

12 oz tomatillos

MEAT & SEAFOOD

1 lb boneless skinless chicken breast

1 lb raw turkey breast

1 lb pork butt or shoulder

1½ lbs salmon

1 1¼-lbs center-cut salmon fillet

1½ lbs striped bass fillets

REFRIGERATOR & DAIRY

½ cup 2% milk

2 cups cottage cheese

17 eggs

¼ cup goat cheese

36 oz, plus 3 Tbsp Greek yogurt

1 cup hummus

½ cup milk

12 cups plain full-fat kefir

½ cup plain yogurt (not Greek)

4 oz ricotta

2 Tbsp unsalted butter

1 cup unsweetened almond milk

2 Tbsp vanilla Greek yogurt

BREAD & BAKERY

4 slices bread*

4 slices pumpernickel

2 slices whole-wheat bread

4 whole-wheat rolls

PANTRY

1 Tbsp anchovy paste

12 oz beer

2 cups brown rice (uncooked)

3 Tbsp capers

1 Tbsp chia seeds

1 Tbsp chicken bouillon

4 tsp coconut flakes (plus more for decorating)

19.5 oz coconut milk

20 oz dark chocolate (72% cacao or higher)

4 oz diced green chilis (canned)

1 28-oz can fire-roasted crushed tomatoes

8 Tbsp hemp seeds

1 8-oz can hominy

4 cups low-sodium chicken broth

1 14-oz can no-salt-added diced tomatoes

4 Tbsp peanut butter

2 tsp prepared horseradish

½ cup quinoa (uncooked)

¼ cup sliced almonds

½ cup unsweetened applesauce

1 15.5-oz can white beans

⅓ cup white chia seeds (or chia seed of choice)

* We used country bread for the Snow Pea and Ricotta Toasts (p. 80), but feel free to use any leftover pumpernickel you might have this week or your favorite loaf.

BREAKFAST

No-Syrup Pancakes (p.76)
+ ½ cup small curd cottage
cheese

SNACK

Stress-Less Smoothie (p.78)

LUNCH

Chopped Egg Salad Toast (p.81)
*Refrigerate remaining in
 airtight container for Day
 4 snack

SNACK

1 apple with 2 Tbsp peanut
butter

DINNER

Chili with Wheat Berries
and Beans (p.87)
*Refrigerate remaining in
 airtight container for Day 2
 lunch

DAILY NUTRITION: 1,722 cal, 91 g
pro, 217 g carb, 40 g fiber, 69.5 g
sugars (0 g added sugars), 59.5 g fat
(21 g sat fat), 0 mg chol, 2,738 mg
sodium

NOTES

_____
_____
_____
_____
_____
_____

WATER

◯ ◯ ◯ ◯ ◯ ◯ ◯ ◯

MOVEMENT/WORKOUT

◯ YES   ◯ NO

ACTIVITY _____
_____
_____

DURATION _____
_____
_____

INTENSITY _____
_____
_____

SLEEP

BEDTIME LAST NIGHT _____

WAKE TIME THIS MORNING _____

SLEEP QUALITY _____
_____

MOOD ☹ 😐 🙂 😀

_____
_____
_____
_____
_____
_____

BREAKFAST

Mango-Coconut Chia Pudding
(p.77)
*Refrigerate remaining in
airtight container for Day 6
breakfast.

SNACK

Berry, Chia, and Mint
Smoothie (p.79)

LUNCH

Chili with Wheat Berries
and Beans (p.87)

SNACK

Snow Pea and Ricotta Toasts
(p.80)
*Refrigerate remaining in
 airtight container for Day
 6 snack

DINNER

Striped Bass with Radish
Salsa Verde (p.89)
*Refrigerate remaining in
 airtight container for Day
 4 dinner

DESSERT

Coconut Truffle (p.96)
*Freeze in airtight
 container for Day 7, 9,
 11, 16, and 24 dessert

DAILY NUTRITION: 1,507 cal, 71 g pro,
166 g carb, 43 g fiber, 52.5 g sugars
(15.5 g added sugars), 67.5 g fat (19.5
g sat fat), 146 mg chol, 1,511 mg sodium

NOTES

_____

_____

WATER

◯ ◯ ◯ ◯ ◯ ◯ ◯ ◯

MOVEMENT/WORKOUT

◯ YES   ◯ NO

ACTIVITY _____

_____

_____

DURATION _____

_____

_____

INTENSITY _____

_____

_____

SLEEP

BEDTIME LAST NIGHT _____

WAKE TIME THIS MORNING _____

SLEEP QUALITY _____

_____

MOOD   ☹ 😐 🙂 😀

_____

_____

_____

_____

BREAKFAST

2 Spinach and Goat Cheese Egg Muffins (p.75) + 6 oz Greek yogurt with ½ cup raspberries

SNACK

Stress-Less Smoothie (p.78)

LUNCH

Salmon Salad with Green Goddess Dressing (p.83)
*Refrigerate remaining in airtight container for Day 5 lunch

SNACK

1 hard-boiled egg on whole-wheat bread

DINNER

Herb-Pounded Chicken with Arugula (p.91)

DAILY NUTRITION: 1,512 cal, 124 g pro, 100 g carb, 23 g fiber, 41 g sugars (0 g added sugars), 68 g fat (18 g sat fat), 773 mg chol, 1,713 mg sodium

NOTES

_____

_____

_____

_____

_____

_____

WATER

◯ ◯ ◯ ◯ ◯ ◯ ◯ ◯

MOVEMENT/WORKOUT

◯ YES ◯ NO

ACTIVITY _____

_____

_____

DURATION _____

_____

_____

INTENSITY _____

_____

_____

SLEEP

BEDTIME LAST NIGHT _____

WAKE TIME THIS MORNING _____

SLEEP QUALITY _____

_____

MOOD ☹ ☺ ☺ ☺

_____

_____

_____

_____

_____

BREAKFAST

◉ No-Syrup Pancakes (p.76)
+ ½ cup small curd cottage
cheese

SNACK

Stress-Less Smoothie (p.78)

LUNCH

Turkey and Greens Soup (p.85)
+ 1 cup brown rice
*Refrigerate remaining in
airtight container for Day
6 lunch

DINNER

◉ Striped Bass with Radish
Salsa Verde (p.89)

DAILY NUTRITION: 1,732 cal, 126 g pro,
152 g carb, 23 g fiber, 45 g sugars (16 g
added sugars), 64.5 g fat (17.5 g sat fat),
341 mg chol, 2,304 mg sodium

NOTES

_____
_____
_____
_____
_____
_____
_____
_____
_____
_____

WATER

◯ ◯ ◯ ◯ ◯ ◯ ◯ ◯

MOVEMENT/WORKOUT

◯ YES   ◯ NO

ACTIVITY _____
_____
_____

DURATION _____
_____

INTENSITY _____
_____
_____

SLEEP

BEDTIME LAST NIGHT _____

WAKE TIME THIS MORNING _____

SLEEP QUALITY _____
_____

MOOD   ☹ 😐 🙂 😃

_____
_____
_____
_____
_____

BREAKFAST

- 2 Spinach and Goat Cheese Egg Muffins (p.75) + 6 oz Greek yogurt with ½ cup raspberries

SNACK

1 cup edamame

LUNCH

- Salmon Salad with Green Goddess Dressing (p.83)

SNACK

1 cup sliced cucumber with 4 Tbsp hummus

DINNER

Slow Cooker Pork Pozole Verde (p.93) + 1 small whole-wheat roll

*Refrigerate remaining in airtight container for Day 7 dinner

DAILY NUTRITION: 1,478 cal, 124 g pro, 134 g carb, 42 g fiber, 28 g sugars (0 g added sugars), 49.5 g fat (12 g sat fat), 512 mg chol, 2,116 mg sodium

NOTES

_____

_____

_____

_____

_____

WATER

◯ ◯ ◯ ◯ ◯ ◯ ◯ ◯

MOVEMENT/WORKOUT

◯ YES   ◯ NO

ACTIVITY _____

_____

DURATION _____

_____

INTENSITY _____

_____

SLEEP

BEDTIME LAST NIGHT _____

WAKE TIME THIS MORNING _____

SLEEP QUALITY _____

_____

MOOD ☹ 😐 🙂 😀

_____

_____

_____

_____

_____

BREAKFAST

Mango-Coconut Chia Pudding (p.77) + 2 Tbsp peanut butter on whole-wheat bread

SNACK

Snow Pea and Ricotta Toasts (p.80)

LUNCH

Turkey and Greens Soup (p.85) + 1 cup brown rice

DINNER

Seared Salmon with Roasted Cauliflower (p.95) + 1 cup quinoa
*Refrigerate remaining in airtight container for Day 7 lunch

DESSERT

Roasted Apples with Greek yogurt (p.97)

DAILY NUTRITION: 1,892 cal, 111 g pro, 217 g carb, 30 g fiber, 56 g sugars (12 g added sugars), 70.5 g fat (17.5 g sat fat), 172 mg chol, 1,574 mg sodium

NOTES

_____
_____
_____
_____
_____
_____

WATER

◯ ◯ ◯ ◯ ◯ ◯ ◯ ◯

MOVEMENT/WORKOUT

◯ YES   ◯ NO

ACTIVITY _____
_____
_____

DURATION _____
_____
_____

INTENSITY _____
_____
_____

SLEEP

BEDTIME LAST NIGHT _____

WAKE TIME THIS MORNING _____

SLEEP QUALITY _____
_____

MOOD ☹ 😐 🙂 😃

_____
_____
_____
_____
_____
_____
_____

BREAKFAST

⊚ 2 Spinach and Goat Cheese Egg Muffins (p.75) + 6 oz Greek yogurt with ½ cup raspberries

SNACK

1 cup sliced cucumber with 4 Tbsp hummus

LUNCH

⊚ Seared Salmon with Roasted Cauliflower (p.95) + 1 cup quinoa

SNACK

Stress-Less Smoothie (p.78)

DINNER

⊚ Slow Cooker Pork Pozole Verde (p.93) + 1 small whole-wheat roll

DESSERT

⊚ Coconut Truffle (p.96)

DAILY NUTRITION: 1,441 cal, 105 g pro, 125 g carb, 32 g fiber, 45 g sugars (5 g added sugars), 55 g fat (17.5 g sat fat), 356 mg chol, 1,794 mg sodium

NOTES

_____
_____
_____
_____
_____

WATER

◯ ◯ ◯ ◯ ◯ ◯ ◯ ◯

MOVEMENT/WORKOUT

◯ YES   ◯ NO

ACTIVITY _____
_____
_____

DURATION _____
_____
_____

INTENSITY _____
_____
_____

SLEEP

BEDTIME LAST NIGHT _____

WAKE TIME THIS MORNING _____

SLEEP QUALITY _____
_____

MOOD ☹ 😐 🙂 😃

_____
_____
_____
_____
_____

WEEK 2 AT A GLANCE

DAY 8

BREAKFAST
1 Apple Oatmeal Muffin +
6 oz Greek yogurt with 1 cup
blueberries

SNACK
Berry, Chia, and Mint Smoothie

LUNCH
Tempeh Lettuce Wraps + 1 oz
vegetable chips (such as Terra)

SNACK
½ cup small curd cottage cheese
+ ½ cup berries

DINNER
Greek Chickpea Tacos

DAY 9

BREAKFAST
Mason Jar Scramble + 2 slices
whole-wheat toast + 1 cup
strawberries

SNACK
Snow Pea and Ricotta Toasts

LUNCH
Greek Chickpea Tacos

SNACK
½ cup Roasted Chickpeas

DINNER
Seared Salmon with
Spiced Sweet Potatoes

DESSERT
Coconut Truffle

DAY 10

BREAKFAST
Mango-Coconut Chia Pudding
+ 1 slice whole-wheat bread
with 2 Tbsp peanut butter

LUNCH
Tempeh Lettuce Wraps + 1 oz
vegetable chips (such as Terra)

SNACK
1 cup sliced cucumber with
4 Tbsp hummus

DINNER
Rainbow Chicken Slaw

DESSERT
Peaches with Honey and Pistachios

DAY 11

BREAKFAST
1 Apple Oatmeal Muffin +
6 oz Greek yogurt with 1 cup
blueberries

SNACK
Tomato Toasts with Mint Yogurt
and Sumac Vinaigrette

LUNCH
Seared Salmon with
Spiced Sweet Potatoes

SNACK
Coconut Truffle

DINNER
Colorful Quinoa Bowls

DAY 12

BREAKFAST
Mason Jar Scramble + 2 slices
whole-wheat toast + 1 cup
strawberries

SNACK
Snow Pea and Ricotta Toasts

LUNCH
Colorful Quinoa Bowls

SNACK
½ cup Roasted Chickpeas

DINNER
Pistachio-Crusted Fish and
Spinach Quinoa

DESSERT
Peaches with Honey and
Pistachios

DAY 13

BREAKFAST
1 Apple Oatmeal Muffin +
6 oz Greek yogurt with
1 cup blueberries

SNACK
1 apple with 2 Tbsp peanut butter

LUNCH
Wild Salmon Salad

SNACK
½ cup small curd cottage
cheese + ½ cup berries

DINNER
Pork and Peach Kebabs with
Grilled Green Beans

DESSERT
2 pieces Blood Orange and
Olive Oil Shortbread

DAY 14

BREAKFAST
Mango-Coconut Chia
Pudding + 1 slice whole-
wheat bread with
2 Tbsp peanut butter

SNACK
Tomato Toasts with Mint
Yogurt and Sumac Vinaigrette

LUNCH
Pork and Peach Kebabs with
Grilled Green Beans

DINNER
Pistachio-Crusted Fish and
Spinach Quinoa

DESSERT
Avocado Mousse

WEEK 2

Below are exact amounts of everything you will need for Week 2. Be sure to check for leftovers from Week 1 before purchasing items from this list. Remember: These lists are for two people. If you're doing the plan by yourself, simply cut the measurements in half.

Shopping List

PRODUCE

2 apples

2½ avocados

4½ cups baby spinach

4 basil leaves

3 medium beets

2 cups berries of choice

2 Tbsp blood orange juice

6 cups blueberries

¾ head Boston lettuce

2 small carrots

1 cup cilantro

3 cloves garlic

1 3-in. piece ginger root

2 Granny Smith apples

2 pints grape tomatoes

1 lb green beans

3 medium heirloom tomatoes

2 lemons

lime (for serving)

1 mango

1 cup, plus 2 Tbsp mint leaves

5 cups mixed greens

2 small onions

½ tsp orange zest

6 peaches

2 small rainbow or Chioggia beets

½ cup raspberries

1 small red cabbage

1 red chile

1½ red onions

4 scallions

1½ seedless cucumbers

2¾ cups snow peas

6 cups strawberries

5 large sweet potatoes

1 large tomato

1 small zucchini

MEAT & SEAFOOD

1¼ lb pork loin

2 4-oz salmon fillets

1½ cups shredded, cooked chicken

1-1¼ lbs skinless salmon fillet

4 6-oz pieces white fish (such as cod or tilapia)

REFRIGERATOR & DAIRY

2 cups, plus 1 Tbsp cottage cheese

6 eggs

14 oz firm tofu

2 tsp horseradish

4 Tbsp hummus

½ cup low-fat buttermilk

2 Tbsp milk

7 cups, plus 1 Tbsp plain Greek yogurt

4 oz ricotta

8 oz roasted tempeh

1 cups unsweetened almond milk

¼ cup white miso

BREAD & BAKERY

4 slices bread

4 whole-wheat pitas

12 slices whole-wheat bread

PANTRY

1 13.5-oz can light coconut milk

1 Tbsp chia seeds

4 tsp coconut flakes

1 Tbsp coriander seeds

2¼ cups confectioners' sugar

2 tsp honey mustard

3 15-oz cans no-salt-added chickpeas

2½ cups old-fashioned oats

¼ cup peach jam

¾ cup peanut butter

1 cup pecans

¼ cup pitted kalamata olives

2¾ cups quinoa

7 Tbsp rice vinegar

1 Tbsp sesame seeds

Shaved chocolate (for serving)

½ cup shelled pistachios (unsalted)

½ cup slivered almonds

4 oz vegetable chips (such as Terra chips)

⅓ cup white chia seeds

¼ cup whole-wheat panko

BREAKFAST

1 Apple Oatmeal Muffin
(p.99) + 6 oz Greek yogurt
with 1 cup blueberries

SNACK

Berry, Chia, and Mint
Smoothie (p.79)

LUNCH

Tempeh Lettuce Wraps (p.105)
+ 1 oz vegetable chips (such
as Terra)
*Refrigerate remaining in
 airtight container for Day
 10 lunch

SNACK

½ cup small curd cottage
cheese + ½ cup berries

DINNER

Greek Chickpea Tacos (p.111)
*Refrigerate remaining in
 airtight container for Day
 9 lunch

DAILY NUTRITION: 1,577 cal, 79 g pro,
201 g carb, 35 g fiber, 51 g sugars (8
g added sugars), 56.5 g fat (10.5 g sat
fat), 51 mg chol, 1,210 mg sodium

NOTES

WATER

○ ○ ○ ○ ○ ○ ○ ○

MOVEMENT/WORKOUT

○ YES   ○ NO

ACTIVITY _____

DURATION _____

INTENSITY _____

SLEEP

BEDTIME LAST NIGHT _____

WAKE TIME THIS MORNING _____

SLEEP QUALITY _____

MOOD ☹ 😐 🙂 😀

BREAKFAST

Mason Jar Scramble (p.100)
+ 2 slices whole-wheat toast
+ 1 cup strawberries

SNACK

Snow Pea and Ricotta Toasts
(p.80)
*Refrigerate remaining in
  airtight container for Day
  12 snack

LUNCH

⊙ Greek Chickpea Tacos
  (p.111)

SNACK

½ cup Roasted Chickpeas
(p.101)
*Store remaining in airtight
  container for Day 12 snack

DINNER

Seared Salmon with Spiced
Sweet Potatoes (p.107)
*Refrigerate remaining in
  airtight container for Day
  11 lunch

DESSERT

⊙ Coconut Truffle (p.96)

DAILY NUTRITION: 1,732 cal, 85 g
pro, 204 g carb, 38 g fiber, 52 g sugars
(8 g added sugars), 70.5 g fat (18.5 g
sat fat), 453 mg chol, 2,791 mg sodium

NOTES

_____
_____
_____

WATER

◯ ◯ ◯ ◯ ◯ ◯ ◯ ◯

MOVEMENT/WORKOUT

◯ YES   ◯ NO

ACTIVITY _____
_____
_____

DURATION _____
_____
_____

INTENSITY _____
_____
_____

SLEEP

BEDTIME LAST NIGHT _____

WAKE TIME THIS MORNING _____

SLEEP QUALITY _____
_____

MOOD ☹ 😐 🙂 😄
_____
_____
_____
_____
_____
_____

BREAKFAST

Mango-Coconut Chia
Pudding (p.77) + 1 slice
whole-wheat bread with
2 Tbsp peanut butter
*Refrigerate remaining in
 airtight container for Day
 14 breakfast

LUNCH

Tempeh Lettuce Wraps
(p.105) + 1 oz vegetable
chips (such as Terra)

SNACK

1 cup sliced cucumber
with 4 Tbsp hummus

DINNER

Rainbow Chicken Slaw
(p.115)

DESSERT

Peaches with Honey and
Pistachios (p.120)
*Refrigerate remaining in
 airtight container for Day
 12 dessert

DAILY NUTRITION: 1,819 cal, 85 g
pro, 187 g carb, 39 g fiber, 75 g sugars
(23 g added sugars), 84.5 g fat (20 g
sat fat), 84 mg chol, 1,139 mg sodium

NOTES

_____
_____
_____
_____

WATER

◯ ◯ ◯ ◯ ◯ ◯ ◯ ◯

MOVEMENT/WORKOUT

◯ YES   ◯ NO

ACTIVITY _____
_____
_____

DURATION _____
_____
_____

INTENSITY _____
_____
_____

SLEEP

BEDTIME LAST NIGHT _____

WAKE TIME THIS MORNING _____

SLEEP QUALITY _____
_____

MOOD ☹ 😐 🙂 😃

_____
_____
_____
_____
_____
_____

BREAKFAST

 1 Apple Oatmeal Muffin (p.99) + 6 oz Greek yogurt with 1 cup blueberries

SNACK

Tomato Toasts with Mint Yogurt and Sumac Vinaigrette (p.103)

LUNCH

Seared Salmon with Spiced Sweet Potatoes (p.107)

SNACK

Coconut Truffle (p.96)

DINNER

Colorful Quinoa Bowls (p.113)
*Refrigerate remaining in airtight container for Day 12 lunch

DAILY NUTRITION: 1,645 cal, 86 g pro, 177 g carb, 31 g fiber, 65 g sugars (14 g added sugars), 70 g fat (14 g sat fat), 112 mg chol, 1,650 mg sodium

NOTES

WATER

○ ○ ○ ○ ○ ○ ○ ○

MOVEMENT/WORKOUT

○ YES ○ NO

ACTIVITY _____

_____

_____

DURATION _____

_____

_____

INTENSITY _____

_____

_____

SLEEP

BEDTIME LAST NIGHT _____

WAKE TIME THIS MORNING _____

SLEEP QUALITY _____

_____

MOOD ☹ 😐 🙂 😀

_____

_____

_____

_____

_____

_____

BREAKFAST
Mason Jar Scramble (p.100)
+ 2 slices whole-wheat toast
+ 1 cup strawberries

SNACK
Snow Pea and Ricotta Toasts
(p.80)

LUNCH
Colorful Quinoa Bowls
(p.113)

SNACK
½ cup Roasted Chickpeas
(p.101)

DINNER
Pistachio-Crusted Fish and
Spinach Quinoa (p.117)
*Refrigerate remaining in
 airtight container for Day
 14 dinner

DESSERT
Peaches with Honey and
Pistachios (p.120)

DAILY NUTRITION: 1,876 cal, 96 g pro,
226 g carb, 39 g fiber, 67 g sugars (11 g
added sugars), 72.5 g fat (11.5 g sat fat),
73 mg chol, 2,478 mg sodium

NOTES

_____

_____

_____

_____

WATER
○ ○ ○ ○ ○ ○ ○ ○

MOVEMENT/WORKOUT
○ YES   ○ NO

ACTIVITY _____

_____

_____

DURATION _____

_____

_____

INTENSITY _____

_____

_____

SLEEP
BEDTIME LAST NIGHT _____

WAKE TIME THIS MORNING _____

SLEEP QUALITY _____

MOOD :(:| :) :D

_____

_____

_____

_____

_____

BREAKFAST
 1 Apple Oatmeal Muffin (p.99) + 6 oz Greek yogurt with 1 cup blueberries

SNACK
1 apple with 2 Tbsp peanut butter

LUNCH
Wild Salmon Salad (p.109)

SNACK
½ cup small curd cottage cheese + ½ cup berries

DINNER
Pork and Peach Kebabs with Grilled Green Beans (p.119)
*Refrigerate remaining in airtight container for Day 14 lunch

DESSERT
2 pieces Blood Orange and Olive Oil Shortbread (p.123)

DAILY NUTRITION: 1,705 cal, 104 g pro, 169 g carb, 36 g fiber, 86 g sugars (32 g added sugars), 79.5 g fat (14 g sat fat), 172 mg chol, 1,157 mg sodium

NOTES

WATER
○ ○ ○ ○ ○ ○ ○ ○

MOVEMENT/WORKOUT
○ YES   ○ NO

ACTIVITY _____

DURATION _____

INTENSITY _____

SLEEP
BEDTIME LAST NIGHT _____

WAKE TIME THIS MORNING _____

SLEEP QUALITY _____

MOOD ☹ 😐 🙂 😀

BREAKFAST

⟳ Mango-Coconut Chia Pudding (p.77) + 1 slice whole-wheat bread with 2 Tbsp peanut butter

SNACK

⟳ Tomato Toasts with Mint Yogurt and Sumac Vinaigrette (p.103)

LUNCH

⟳ Pork and Peach Kebabs with Grilled Green Beans (p.119)

DINNER

⟳ Pistachio-Crusted Fish and Spinach Quinoa (p.117)

DESSERT

Avocado Mousse (p.121)

DAILY NUTRITION: 1,804 cal, 96 g pro, 169 g carb, 37 g fiber, 75.5 g sugars (49.1 g added sugars), 92 g fat (20.5 g sat fat), 145 mg chol, 1,306 mg sodium

NOTES

WATER

◯ ◯ ◯ ◯ ◯ ◯ ◯ ◯

MOVEMENT/WORKOUT

◯ YES   ◯ NO

ACTIVITY _____

DURATION _____

INTENSITY _____

SLEEP

BEDTIME LAST NIGHT _____

WAKE TIME THIS MORNING _____

SLEEP QUALITY _____

MOOD ☹ 😐 🙂 😃

Leftovers

DAY 15

BREAKFAST
Banana and Almond Butter Pancakes + 6 oz Greek yogurt with ½ cup raspberries

SNACK
1 apple with 2 Tbsp peanut butter

LUNCH
Spinach and Cheese Naan Pizzas and Tomato Salad

DINNER
Spring Minestrone Soup with Homemade Pesto

DESSERT
Avocado Mousse

DAY 16

BREAKFAST
Blueberry and Mixed Nut Parfait

SNACK
Tomato Toasts with Mint Yogurt and Sumac Vinaigrette

LUNCH
Shrimp, Avocado, and Egg Chopped Salad

SNACK
1 Coconut Truffle

DINNER
Greek Chicken Tacos

DAY 17

BREAKFAST
Curry-Avocado Crispy Egg Toast

SNACK
1 cup sliced celery with 4 Tbsp hummus

LUNCH
Greek Chicken Tacos

SNACK
Berry, Chia, and Mint Smoothie

DINNER
Honey-Spiced Salmon with Quinoa

DAY 18

BREAKFAST
Banana and Almond Butter Pancakes + 6 oz Greek yogurt with ½ cup raspberries

SNACK
½ cup small curd cottage cheese with ½ cup berries

LUNCH
Shrimp, Avocado, and Egg Chopped Salad

SNACK
Snow Pea and Ricotta Toasts

DINNER
Grilled Yogurt-Marinated Chicken + 1 cup steamed broccoli

DESSERT
1 serving Dark Chocolate Power Bark

DAY 19

BREAKFAST
Curry-Avocado Crispy Egg Toast

SNACK
Stress-Less Smoothie

LUNCH
Grilled Yogurt-Marinated Chicken

SNACK
1 cup sliced celery with 4 Tbsp hummus

DINNER
Honey-Spiced Salmon with Quinoa

DAY 20

BREAKFAST
Blueberry and Mixed Nut Parfait

SNACK
Tomato Toasts with Mint Yogurt and Sumac Vinaigrette

LUNCH
Spring Minestrone Soup with Homemade Pesto

DINNER
Green Envy Rice Bowl

DESSERT
1 serving Dark Chocolate Power Bark

DAY 21

BREAKFAST
Curry-Avocado Crispy Egg Toast + 6 oz Greek yogurt with ½ cup raspberries

SNACKS
Snow Pea and Ricotta Toasts

LUNCH
Green Envy Rice Bowl

SNACK
Stress-Less Smoothie

DINNER
Spring Minestrone Soup with Homemade Pesto

Below are exact amounts of everything you will need for Week 3. Be sure to check for leftovers from Week 2 before purchasing items from this list. Remember: These lists are for two people. If you're doing the plan by yourself, simply cut the measurements in half.

Shopping List

PRODUCE

1 apple

2 lbs asparagus

4 avocados

½ cup berries of choice

2 cups broccoli

½ lb Brussels sprouts

8 cups butter lettuce

1 cup celery

½ cup, plus 6 Tbsp cilantro

½ cucumber

1 cup, plus 1 Tbsp dill

1 small fennel bulb

3 1-in. pieces fresh ginger

1 lemon

8 limes

9 cloves garlic

1 cup grape tomatoes

8 oz green beans

2 leeks

1 medium beet

3 medium heirloom tomatoes

1 cup mint

½ lb mushrooms (cremini or button)

1 onion

1 orange

2 peaches

4½ cups raspberries

1 small head red cabbage

2 ripe bananas

3 scallions

¼ small red onion

4 oz snow peas

½ small bunch spinach

1 cup strawberries

4 oz sugar snap peas

1 tomato, plus ½ lb tomatoes

MEAT & SEAFOOD

4 lbs chicken

1 lb ground chicken

12 oz peeled and deveined large shrimp

1 rotisserie chicken

1½ lbs salmon fillet

REFRIGERATOR & DAIRY

11 large eggs

2 oz feta

8½ cups Greek yogurt

2 tsp horseradish

12 Tbsp hummus

1 cup kimchi

1 tsp miso paste

2 oz Parmesan

½ cups plain full-fat kefir, chilled

1 cup plain yogurt

⅓ oz ricotta

½ cup small curd cottage cheese

1½ oz thinly sliced provolone

1 cup, plus 3 Tbsp unsweetened almond milk

BREAD & BAKERY

1 piece naan or pita bread

12 slices whole-grain bread

4 pieces whole-wheat pita bread

PANTRY

3 Tbsp almonds

1 cup brown rice (uncooked)

1 15-oz can cannellini beans

⅛ tsp cardamom

¼ cup cashews

1 Tbsp chia seeds

¼ cup, plus 3 Tbsp pecans

1½ tsp curry powder

14 oz dark chocolate (70% cacao or higher)

1 cup freeze-dried blueberries

¼ cup golden raisins

¾ cup granola

1½ Tbsp ground coriander

2 Tbsp hemp seeds

3½ Tbsp low-sodium vegetable base

2 Tbsp peanut butter

3 Tbsp pepitas

1 cup quinoa

Shaved chocolate (for serving)

1 tsp smoked paprika

6 Tbsp smooth almond butter

½ cup tahini

¾ cup tart cherries

3 Tbsp walnuts

BREAKFAST

Banana and Almond Butter Pancakes (p.125) + 6 oz Greek yogurt with ½ cup raspberries
*Refrigerate remaining in airtight container for Day 18 breakfast

LUNCH

Spinach and Cheese Naan Pizzas and Tomato Salad (p.131)

SNACK

1 apple with 2 Tbsp peanut butter

DINNER

Spring Minestrone Soup with Homemade Pesto (p.135)
*Freeze remaining in airtight container for Day 20 lunch and Day 21 dinner

DESSERT

Avocado Mousse (p.121)

DAILY NUTRITION: 1,768 cal, 68 g pro, 170 g carb, 42 g fiber, 87 g sugars (35.5 g added sugars), 96.5 g fat (19 g sat fat), 183 mg chol, 1,700 mg sodium

NOTES

_____
_____
_____
_____
_____

WATER

◯ ◯ ◯ ◯ ◯ ◯ ◯ ◯

MOVEMENT/WORKOUT

◯ YES   ◯ NO

ACTIVITY _____
_____
_____

DURATION _____
_____
_____

INTENSITY _____
_____
_____

SLEEP

BEDTIME LAST NIGHT _____
WAKE TIME THIS MORNING _____
SLEEP QUALITY _____
_____

MOOD   ☹ 😐 🙂 😃

_____
_____
_____
_____
_____
_____

BREAKFAST

Blueberry and Mixed Nut
Parfait (p.127)
*Refrigerate remaining in
 airtight container for Day
 20 breakfast

SNACK

Tomato Toasts with
Mint Yogurt and Sumac
Vinaigrette (p.103)
*Refrigerate remaining in
 airtight container for Day
 20 snack

LUNCH

Shrimp, Avocado, and Egg
Chopped Salad (p.133)
*Refrigerate remaining in
 airtight container for Day
 18 lunch

SNACK

⊙ Coconut Truffle (p.96)

DINNER

Greek Chicken Tacos (p.137)
*Refrigerate remaining in
 airtight container for Day
 17 lunch

DAILY NUTRITION: 1,512 cal, 103 g
pro, 109 g carb, 22 g fiber, 44 g sugars
(4.5 g added sugars), 79 g fat (24 g sat
fat), 590 mg chol, 1,743 mg sodium

NOTES

_____
_____
_____
_____

WATER

◯ ◯ ◯ ◯ ◯ ◯ ◯ ◯

MOVEMENT/WORKOUT

◯ YES   ◯ NO

ACTIVITY _____
_____
_____

DURATION _____
_____
_____

INTENSITY _____
_____
_____

SLEEP

BEDTIME LAST NIGHT _____

WAKE TIME THIS MORNING _____

SLEEP QUALITY _____
_____

MOOD ☹ 😐 🙂 😀

_____
_____
_____
_____
_____
_____

BREAKFAST
Curry-Avocado Crispy Egg
Toast (p.129)

SNACK
1 cup sliced celery with
4 Tbsp hummus

LUNCH
 Greek Chicken Tacos (p.137)

SNACK
Berry, Chia, and Mint
Smoothie (p.79)

DINNER
Honey-Spiced Salmon with
Quinoa (p.139)
*Refrigerate remaining in
 airtight container for Day
 19 dinner

DAILY NUTRITION: 1,570 cal, 92 g pro,
134 g carb, 30 g fiber, 23 g sugars (6
g added sugars), 76.5 g fat (14.5 g sat
fat), 361 mg chol, 1,684 mg sodium

NOTES

_____

_____

_____

_____

_____

_____

WATER

○ ○ ○ ○ ○ ○ ○ ○

MOVEMENT/WORKOUT

○ YES   ○ NO

ACTIVITY _____

_____

DURATION _____

_____

INTENSITY _____

_____

SLEEP

BEDTIME LAST NIGHT _____

WAKE TIME THIS MORNING _____

SLEEP QUALITY _____

_____

MOOD   ☹ 😐 🙂 😀

_____

_____

_____

_____

DAY 18

BREAKFAST
🔄 Banana and Almond Butter Pancakes (p.125) + 6 oz Greek yogurt with ½ cup raspberries

SNACK
½ cup small curd cottage cheese with ½ cup berries

LUNCH
🔄 Shrimp, Avocado, and Egg Chopped Salad (p.133)

SNACK
Snow Pea and Ricotta Toasts (p.80)
*Refrigerate remaining in airtight container for Day 21 snack

DINNER
Grilled Yogurt-Marinated Chicken (p.141) + 1 cup steamed broccoli
*Refrigerate remaining in airtight container for Day 19 lunch

DESSERT
🔄 1 serving Dark Chocolate Power Bark (p.145)

DAILY NUTRITION: 1,845 cal, 130 g pro, 138 g carb, 32 g fiber, 70 g sugars (37 g added sugars), 74.5 g fat (35.5 g sat fat), 731 mg chol, 1,747 mg sodium

NOTES

_____

_____

WATER

◯ ◯ ◯ ◯ ◯ ◯ ◯ ◯

MOVEMENT/WORKOUT
◯ YES   ◯ NO

ACTIVITY _____

_____

_____

DURATION _____

_____

_____

INTENSITY _____

_____

_____

SLEEP
BEDTIME LAST NIGHT _____

WAKE TIME THIS MORNING _____

SLEEP QUALITY _____

_____

MOOD ☹ 😐 🙂 😄

_____

_____

_____

_____

_____

_____

60 28-DAY ANTI-INFLAMMATORY DIET

BREAKFAST
Curry-Avocado Crispy Egg Toast (p.129)

SNACK
Stress-Less Smoothie (p.78)

LUNCH
 Grilled Yogurt-Marinated Chicken (p.141) + 1 cup steamed broccoli

SNACK
1 cup sliced celery with 4 Tbsp hummus

DINNER
 Honey-Spiced Salmon with Quinoa (p.139)

DAILY NUTRITION: 1,645 cal, 106 g pro, 114 g carb, 26 g fiber, 35 g sugars (6 g added sugars), 85.5 g fat (18 g sat fat), 395 mg chol, 1,717 mg sodium

NOTES

_____
_____
_____
_____
_____
_____
_____
_____

WATER
○ ○ ○ ○ ○ ○ ○ ○

MOVEMENT/WORKOUT
○ YES   ○ NO

ACTIVITY _____
_____
_____

DURATION _____
_____
_____

INTENSITY _____
_____
_____

SLEEP
BEDTIME LAST NIGHT _____
WAKE TIME THIS MORNING _____
SLEEP QUALITY _____
_____

MOOD ☹ 😐 🙂 😃
_____
_____
_____
_____
_____
_____

BREAKFAST

⟳ Blueberry and Mixed Nut Parfait (p.127)

SNACK

⟳ Tomato Toasts with Mint Yogurt and Sumac Vinaigrette (p.103)

LUNCH

⟳ Spring Minestrone Soup with Homemade Pesto (p.135)

DINNER

Green Envy Rice Bowl (p.143)
*Refrigerate remaining in airtight container for Day 21 lunch

DESSERT

1 serving Dark Chocolate Power Bark (p.145)

DAILY NUTRITION: 1,714 cal, 78 g pro, 146 g carb, 31 g fiber, 59 g sugars (18 g added sugars), 91.5 g fat (37.5 g sat fat), 89 mg chol, 1,808 mg sodium

NOTES

_____
_____
_____
_____
_____
_____

WATER

◯ ◯ ◯ ◯ ◯ ◯ ◯ ◯

MOVEMENT/WORKOUT

◯ YES   ◯ NO

ACTIVITY _____
_____
_____

DURATION _____
_____
_____

INTENSITY _____
_____
_____

SLEEP

BEDTIME LAST NIGHT _____

WAKE TIME THIS MORNING _____

SLEEP QUALITY _____
_____

MOOD ☹ 😐 🙂 😄

_____
_____
_____
_____
_____
_____
_____

BREAKFAST
Curry-Avocado Crispy Egg
Toast (p.129) + 6 oz Greek
yogurt with ½ cup raspberries

SNACK
◉ Snow Pea and Ricotta Toasts
(p.80)

LUNCH
◉ Green Envy Rice Bowl
(p.143)

SNACK
Stress-Less Smoothie (p.78)

DINNER
◉ Spring Minestrone Soup
with Homemade Pesto
(p.135)

DAILY NUTRITION: 1,767 cal, 89.4 g
pro, 147 g carb, 41 g fiber, 50 g sugars
(2 g added sugars), 91 g fat (18.5 g sat
fat), 276 mg chol, 2,030 mg sodium

NOTES

_____
_____
_____
_____
_____
_____
_____
_____

WATER
○ ○ ○ ○ ○ ○ ○ ○

MOVEMENT/WORKOUT
○ YES   ○ NO

ACTIVITY _____
_____
_____

DURATION _____
_____
_____

INTENSITY _____
_____
_____

SLEEP

BEDTIME LAST NIGHT _____

WAKE TIME THIS MORNING _____

SLEEP QUALITY _____
_____

MOOD ☹ 😐 🙂 😀
_____
_____
_____
_____
_____

WEEK 4 AT A GLANCE

Leftovers

DAY 22

BREAKFAST
Strawberry-Thyme Millet Bowl

SNACK
Berry, Chia, and Mint Smoothie

LUNCH
Spinach-Curry Crepes with
Apple, Raisins, and Chickpeas

SNACK
½ cup small curd cottage cheese
with ½ cup berries

DINNER
Grain Bowl with Sautéed
Spinach

DESSERT
1 serving Dark
Chocolate Power Bark

DAY 23

BREAKFAST
Sunny-Side-Up Eggs on
Garlicky Greens + 1 slice
whole-wheat toast

SNACK
Mango-Coconut Chia
Pudding

LUNCH
Roast Chicken Salad with
Butternut Squash and Farro

SNACK
Spinach-Curry Crepes
with Apple, Raisins, and
Chickpeas

DINNER
Seared Tilapia with Spiralized
Zucchini

DAY 24

BREAKFAST
2 Veggie-Loaded Chickpea Waffles

SNACK
Stress-Less Smoothie

LUNCH
Seared Tilapia with Spiralized
Zucchini

SNACK
Tomato Toasts with Mint Yogurt
and Sumac Vinaigrette

DINNER
Roast Chicken Salad with
Butternut Squash and Farro

DESSERT
1 Coconut Truffle

DAY 25

BREAKFAST
Strawberry-Thyme Millet Bowl

SNACK
Tomato Toasts with Mint Yogurt
and Sumac Vinaigrette

LUNCH
Chicken and Blueberry
Chimichurri Skewers

SNACK
Berry, Chia, and Mint Smoothie

DINNER
Quick Seafood Stew

DESSERT
Avocado Mousse

DAY 26

BREAKFAST
Sunny-Side-Up Eggs on
Garlicky Greens + 1 slice
whole-wheat toast

SNACK
Tomato Toasts with Mint Yogurt
and Sumac Vinaigrette

LUNCH
Grain Bowl with Sautéed
Spinach

DINNER
Orange Chicken and Broccoli
Stir-Fry

DESSERT
2 pieces Blood Orange
and Olive Oil Shortbread

DAY 27

BREAKFAST
Veggie-Loaded Chickpea
Waffles + 1 cup strawberries

SNACK
Mango-Coconut Chia Pudding

LUNCH
Roast Chicken Salad with
Butternut Squash and Farro
+ Chicken and Blueberry
Chimichurri Skewers

DINNER
Quick Seafood Stew

DAY 28

BREAKFAST
Strawberry-Thyme Millet Bowl

SNACK
Berry, Chia, and Mint Smoothie

LUNCH
Chicken and Blueberry
Chimichurri Skewers

SNACK
Tomato Toasts with Mint
Yogurt and Sumac Vinaigrette

DINNER
Almond-Crusted Striped Bass

DESSERT
Avocado Mousse

64 28-DAY ANTI-INFLAMMATORY DIET

WEEK 4

Below are exact amounts of everything you will need for Week 4. Be sure to check for leftovers from Week 3 before purchasing items from this list. Remember: These lists are for two people. If you're doing the plan by yourself, simply cut the measurements in half.

Shopping List

PRODUCE

2½ avocados

8 cups baby arugula

5½ cups baby spinach

12 oz blueberries

1 lb broccoli crowns

½ medium butternut squash

½ bunch cilantro

6 cups dark leafy greens

1 bulb fennel

1¾ cups flat leaf parsley

1 Tbsp fresh oregano

4 sprigs fresh thyme

12½ cloves garlic

2 tsp ginger

1 Granny Smith apple

3 medium heirloom tomatoes

2 lemons

1 lime

1 mango

3 medium beets

1¼ cups mint

6 cups mixed greens

1 onion

2 medium parsnips

2 peaches

4 small radishes

2½ cups raspberries

1 red bell pepper

8 scallions

1 cup seedless red grapes

2 medium shallots

12½ cups strawberries

1 medium tomato

1½ lbs zucchini

MEAT & SEAFOOD

4 5-oz boneless, skinless striped bass fillets

½ lb chicken tenders

8 oz cod

1 lb grilled chicken breast

½ lb mussels

½ lb peeled and deveined shrimp

1 rotisserie chicken

4 small tilapia fillets

REFRIGERATOR & DAIRY

1¼ cups 1% milk

½ cup 2% plain Greek yogurt

2 cups 2% milk (plus more for serving)

3 cups, plus 3 Tbsp unsweetened almond milk

½ cup cottage cheese

10 eggs

3 tsp grated Parmesan cheese

½ cup orange juice

3 cups plain full-fat kefir

½ cup plain Greek yogurt

3 oz soft goat cheese

BREAD & BAKERY

Crusty bread (for serving)

8 slices whole-wheat bread

PANTRY

¼ tsp allspice

⅔ cup blanched almonds

¾ cup brown rice (uncooked)

1 13.5-oz can coconut milk

1 Tbsp capers

3 Tbsp chia seeds

½ cup chickpea flour

1 15.5-oz can chickpeas

1 tsp cornstarch

1 14-oz can crushed tomatoes

1 cup dry white wine

1 cup farro

2 Tbsp golden raisins

6 Tbsp hemp seeds

5 Tbsp honey

2 cups leftover cooked grains (brown rice, quinoa, farro)

1 Tbsp madras curry powder

2 cups millet

1 Tbsp orange marmalade

¼ cup pumpkin seeds

1 cup quinoa

¼ cup reduced-sodium chicken broth

2 cups reduced-sodium chicken broth or seafood stock

1 Tbsp reduced-sodium soy sauce

Shaved chocolate (for serving)

4 Tbsp shelled pistachios

¼ cup sliced almonds

1¼ tsp smoked paprika

⅓ cup white chia seeds

BREAKFAST

Strawberry-Thyme Millet Bowl
(p.146)
*Refrigerate remaining in
airtight container for Day
25 breakfast

SNACK

Berry, Chia, and Mint
Smoothie (p.79)

LUNCH

Spinach-Curry Crepes
with Apple, Raisins, and
Chickpeas (p.151)
*Refrigerate remaining in
airtight container for Day
23 snack

SNACK

½ cup small curd cottage
cheese with ½ cup berries

DINNER

Grain Bowl with Sautéed
Spinach (p.157)

DESSERT

1 serving Dark Chocolate
Power Bark (p.145)

DAILY NUTRITION: 1,702 cal, 57 g pro,
219 g carb, 40 g fiber, 56 g sugars (23 g
added sugars), 61.5 g fat (29.5 g sat fat),
243 mg chol, 1,029 mg sodium

NOTES

_____

_____

_____

WATER

◯ ◯ ◯ ◯ ◯ ◯ ◯ ◯

MOVEMENT/WORKOUT

◯ YES   ◯ NO

ACTIVITY _____

_____

_____

DURATION _____

_____

_____

INTENSITY _____

_____

_____

SLEEP

BEDTIME LAST NIGHT _____

WAKE TIME THIS MORNING _____

SLEEP QUALITY _____

_____

MOOD   ☹ 😐 🙂 😀

_____

_____

_____

_____

_____

DAY 23

BREAKFAST
Sunny-Side-Up Eggs on
Garlicky Greens (p.147) +
1 slice whole-wheat toast

SNACK
Mango-Coconut Chia
Pudding (p.77)
*Refrigerate remaining in
 airtight container for Day
 27 snack

LUNCH
Roast Chicken Salad with
Butternut Squash and Farro
(p.153)
*Refrigerate remaining in
 airtight container for Day
 24 dinner

SNACK
 Spinach-Curry Crepes
 with Apple, Raisins, and
 Chickpeas (p.151)

DINNER
Seared Tilapia with
Spiralized Zucchini (p.159)
*Refrigerate remaining in
 airtight container for Day
 24 lunch

DAILY NUTRITION: 1,760 cal, 99 g pro,
169 g carb, 31 g fiber, 60 g sugars (9 g
added sugars), 83 g fat (22 g sat fat),
499 mg chol, 1,668 mg sodium

NOTES
_____
_____
_____

WATER
◯ ◯ ◯ ◯ ◯ ◯ ◯ ◯

MOVEMENT/WORKOUT
◯ YES   ◯ NO

ACTIVITY _____
_____
_____

DURATION _____
_____
_____

INTENSITY _____
_____
_____

SLEEP
BEDTIME LAST NIGHT _____
WAKE TIME THIS MORNING _____
SLEEP QUALITY _____
_____

MOOD ☹ 😐 🙂 😀
_____
_____
_____
_____

BREAKFAST

2 Veggie-Loaded Chickpea
Waffles (p.149)
*Refrigerate remaining in
airtight container for Day
27 breakfast

SNACK

Stress-Less Smoothie (p.78)

LUNCH

◉ Seared Tilapia with
Spiralized Zucchini (p.159)

SNACK

Tomato Toasts with
Mint Yogurt and Sumac
Vinaigrette (p.103)
*Refrigerate remaining in
airtight container for Day
25 snack

DINNER

◉ Roast Chicken Salad with
Butternut Squash and Farro
(p.153)

DESSERT

◉ 1 Coconut Truffle (p.96)

DAILY NUTRITION: 1,587 cal, 100 g pro,
134 g carb, 25.5 g fiber, 55 g sugars (5 g
added sugars), 78.5 g fat (23.5 g sat fat),
476 mg chol, 1,355 mg sodium

NOTES

_____

_____

_____

WATER

◯ ◯ ◯ ◯ ◯ ◯ ◯ ◯

MOVEMENT/WORKOUT

◯ YES   ◯ NO

ACTIVITY _____

_____

_____

DURATION _____

_____

_____

INTENSITY _____

_____

_____

SLEEP

BEDTIME LAST NIGHT _____

WAKE TIME THIS MORNING _____

SLEEP QUALITY _____

_____

MOOD ☹ 😐 🙂 😀

_____

_____

_____

_____

_____

_____

DAY 25

BREKFAST
🔄 Strawberry-Thyme Millet Bowl (p.146)

SNACK
🔄 Tomato Toasts with Mint Yogurt and Sumac Vinaigrette (p.103)

LUNCH
Chicken and Blueberry Chimichurri Skewers (p.155)
*Refrigerate remaining in airtight container for Day 27 lunch

SNACK
Berry, Chia, and Mint Smoothie (p.79)

DINNER
Quick Seafood Stew (p.161)
*Refrigerate remaining in airtight container for Day 27 dinner

DESSERT
Avocado Mousse (p.121)

DAILY NUTRITION: 1,556 cal, 78 g pro, 168 g carb, 39 g fiber, 60 g sugars (22.5 g added sugars), 71 g fat (11 g sat fat), 165 mg chol, 1,626 mg sodium

NOTES

_____
_____
_____

WATER
◯ ◯ ◯ ◯ ◯ ◯ ◯ ◯

MOVEMENT/WORKOUT
◯ YES   ◯ NO

ACTIVITY _____
_____
_____

DURATION _____
_____
_____

INTENSITY _____
_____
_____

SLEEP
BEDTIME LAST NIGHT _____
WAKE TIME THIS MORNING _____
SLEEP QUALITY _____
_____

MOOD ☹ 😐 🙂 😀

_____
_____
_____
_____
_____

BREAKFAST
Sunny-Side-Up Eggs on
Garlicky Greens (p.147) +
1 slice whole-wheat toast

LUNCH
Grain Bowl with Sautéed
Spinach (p.157)

SNACK
Tomato Toasts with Mint
Yogurt and Sumac Vinaigrette
(p.103)

DINNER
Orange Chicken and Broccoli
Stir-Fry (p.163)

DESSERT
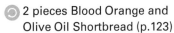 2 pieces Blood Orange and
Olive Oil Shortbread (p.123)

DAILY NUTRITION: 1,636 cal, 71 g pro,
179 g carb, 28 g fiber, 35.5 g sugars (12
g added sugars), 75.5 g fat (13 g sat
fat), 461 mg chol, 1,615 mg sodium

WATER

◯ ◯ ◯ ◯ ◯ ◯ ◯ ◯

MOVEMENT/WORKOUT
◯ YES   ◯ NO

ACTIVITY _____

_____

_____

DURATION _____

_____

_____

INTENSITY _____

_____

_____

SLEEP
BEDTIME LAST NIGHT _____

WAKE TIME THIS MORNING _____

SLEEP QUALITY _____

_____

MOOD ☹ 😐 🙂 😄

_____

_____

_____

_____

_____

_____

NOTES

_____

_____

_____

_____

_____

_____

_____

_____

BREAKFAST

- Veggie-Loaded Chickpea Waffles (p.149) + 1 cup strawberries

SNACK

- Mango-Coconut Chia Pudding (p.77)

LUNCH

- Roast Chicken Salad with Butternut Squash and Farro (p.153)
  Chicken and Blueberry Chimichurri Skewers (p.155)

DINNER

- Quick Seafood Stew (p.161)

DAILY NUTRITION: 1,729 cal, 103 g pro, 172 g carb, 30 g fiber, 71 g sugars (9 g added sugars), 75.5 g fat (21 g sat fat), 523 mg chol, 1,808 mg sodium

NOTES

_____
_____
_____
_____
_____
_____
_____
_____
_____

WATER

◯ ◯ ◯ ◯ ◯ ◯ ◯ ◯

MOVEMENT/WORKOUT

◯ YES   ◯ NO

ACTIVITY _____
_____

DURATION _____
_____

INTENSITY _____
_____

SLEEP

BEDTIME LAST NIGHT _____

WAKE TIME THIS MORNING _____

SLEEP QUALITY _____
_____

MOOD   ☹ 😐 🙂 😀

_____
_____
_____
_____

BREAKFAST

Strawberry-Thyme Millet Bowl
(p.146)

SNACK

Berry, Chia, and Mint
Smoothie (p.79)

LUNCH

Chicken and Blueberry
Chimichurri Skewers (p.155)

SNACK

 Tomato Toasts with
Mint Yogurt and Sumac
Vinaigrette (p.103)

DINNER

Almond-Crusted Striped
Bass (p.165)

DESSERT

Avocado Mousse (p.121)

DAILY NUTRITION: 1,628 cal, 81 g pro,
161 g carb, 40 g fiber, 55 g sugars (23 g
added sugars), 81 g fat (12 g sat fat), 175
mg chol, 1,166 mg sodium

NOTES

_____

_____

_____

_____

_____

WATER

◯ ◯ ◯ ◯ ◯ ◯ ◯ ◯

MOVEMENT/WORKOUT

◯ YES   ◯ NO

ACTIVITY _____

_____

_____

DURATION _____

_____

_____

INTENSITY _____

_____

_____

SLEEP

BEDTIME LAST NIGHT _____

WAKE TIME THIS MORNING _____

SLEEP QUALITY _____

_____

MOOD 😦 😐 🙂 😃

_____

_____

_____

_____

_____

PART 4

RECIPES

SPINACH AND GOAT CHEESE EGG MUFFINS

Eggs and goat cheese pack a morning protein punch that will keep your blood sugar levels steady all day long. You'll get a dose of antioxidant-rich polyphenols from the spinach and bell peppers too.

ACTIVE 15 MIN.   TOTAL 45 MIN.   SERVES 6

1   Tbsp extra virgin olive oil

1   large red pepper, cut into ¼-in. pieces

    Kosher salt and pepper

2   scallions, chopped

6   large eggs

½   cup milk

1   5-oz pkg. baby spinach, chopped

¼   cup fresh goat cheese, crumbled

PER 2 EGG MUFFINS: 130 cal, 8 g pro, 4 g carb, 2 g fiber, 2 g sugars (0 g added sugars), 9 g fat (3 g sat fat), 194 mg chol, 240 mg sodium

1. Heat oven to 350°F. Spray 12-cup muffin pan with nonstick cooking spray.

2. In a large skillet, heat oil on medium. Add red pepper and ⅛ tsp each salt and pepper and cook, covered, stirring occasionally, until tender, 6 to 8 min. Remove from heat and stir in scallions.

3. In a large bowl, beat together eggs, milk, ¼ tsp salt, and ⅛ tsp pepper. Stir in spinach and red pepper mixture.

4. Divide batter among muffin pan cups (about ¼ cup each), top with goat cheese, and bake until just set in the center, 20 to 25 min. (Even when set, tops of muffins may look wet from the spinach.)

5. Cool on wire rack 5 min., then remove from pan. Serve warm. Can be refrigerated up to 4 days; microwave on high 30 seconds to reheat.

NO-SYRUP PANCAKES

Thinly sliced apple rings pressed into the center of each pancake get warm, gooey, and caramelized while the pancakes cook. No need for sugary toppings here!

ACTIVE 25 MIN.   TOTAL 25 MIN.   SERVES 4

1   cup all-purpose flour
2   tsp baking powder
½   tsp ground cinnamon
½   tsp kosher salt
½   cup 2% milk, at
     room temp
½   cup unsweetened applesauce
2   Tbsp unsalted butter, melted
1   large egg, at room temp
     Canola oil, for pan
1   large apple (we used Gala), peeled and cut into thin rounds, then cored

PER SERVING: 245 cal, 7 g pro, 36 g carb, 2 g fiber, 10 g sugars (0 g added sugars), 9 g fat (5 g sat fat), 67 mg chol, 635 mg sodium

1   In small bowl, whisk together flour, baking powder, cinnamon, and salt.

2   In medium bowl, whisk together milk, applesauce, butter, and egg. Add dry ingredients to wet ones and mix until just combined. (Batter should be slightly lumpy.)

3   Lightly coat large nonstick skillet with oil and heat on medium. Spoon 3 scant ¼-cupfuls batter into skillet and place 1 apple ring in each, pushing rings in slightly. Cook until bubbles begin to appear around edges, 2 to 3 min.

4   Using spatula to lift, peek underneath to be sure bottoms are golden brown, then carefully flip. Cook until browned on other side, about 1 min. more. Transfer to wire rack and cover loosely with foil to keep warm. Repeat with remaining apple rings and batter.

MANGO-COCONUT CHIA PUDDING

Loaded with omega-3s (thanks, chia seeds!), this creamy, no-cook pudding makes it easy to fill up on inflammation-fighting fats first thing in the morning.

ACTIVE 12 MIN.
TOTAL 1 HR. 12 MIN. PLUS CHILLING
SERVES 4

1	13.5-oz can light coconut milk
⅓	cup white chia seeds
2	Tbsp honey
1	tsp pure vanilla extract
1	mango, peeled, pitted, and diced
1	cup strawberries, diced
¼	cup sliced almonds
4	tsp coconut flakes

1 In a pint-size measuring cup, combine coconut milk, chia seeds, honey, and vanilla. Stir until combined, then refrigerate for 1 hr.

2 Layer fruit over pudding. Top with a spoonful of strawberries, sliced almonds, and a sprinkle of coconut.

PER SERVING: 273 cal, 7 g pro, 33 g carb, 7 g fiber, 24 g sugars (9 g added sugars), 14 g fat (7 g sat fat), 0 mg chol, 10 mg sodium

STRESS-LESS SMOOTHIE

The protein from the kefir and hemp seeds will stave off blood sugar spikes and afternoon cookie cravings. And the fruit offers antioxidants such as vitamin C.

ACTIVE 5 MIN. TOTAL 5 MIN. SERVES 2

3   cups plain full-fat kefir, chilled

1   cup raspberries

2   Tbsp hemp seeds

2   peaches, pitted and sliced

1   cup ice

1 In blender, puree kefir, raspberries, hemp seeds, peach, and ice until smooth, about 30 seconds.

PER SERVING: 222 cal, 9 g pro, 29 g carb, 6 g fiber, 21 g sugars (0 g added sugars), 9 g fat (3 g sat fat), 18 mg chol, 54 mg sodium

BERRY, CHIA & MINT SMOOTHIE

That pretty pink color from the raspberries, strawberries, and beets lets you know that this cool, creamy sipper is all about the antioxidants.

ACTIVE 10 MIN.   TOTAL 10 MIN. PLUS FREEZING   SERVES 2

1 cup sliced strawberries
½ cup raspberries
½ cup grated beet (from 1 medium beet)
⅓ cup mint leaves
1 Tbsp chia seeds
1 cup unsweetened almond milk

1 In a resealable plastic bag or freezer-safe jar, place berries, beet, mint, and chia seeds. Freeze overnight or longer.

2 When ready to prepare, add almond milk to blender, then add frozen ingredients. Blend until smooth. Serve in 2 tall glasses.

PER SERVING: 105 cal, 3 g pro, 17 g carb, 8 g fiber, 7 g sugars (0 g added sugars), 3.5 g fat (0.5 g sat fat), 0 mg chol, 115 mg sodium

SNOW PEA AND RICOTTA TOASTS

The combo of creamy, high-protein ricotta and fiber-packed snow peas on warm toast makes for a satisfying anti-inflammatory snack.

ACTIVE 10 MIN.   **TOTAL 10 MIN.**   **SERVES 4**

- 4 oz snow peas
- 1 Tbsp white wine vinegar
- 1 Tbsp olive oil
- 2 tsp prepared horseradish
- ½ tsp honey
- ½ tsp salt
- 4 slices toasted bread *
- 1 oz ricotta

1. Slice snow peas crosswise ¼ in. thick. In a bowl, whisk peas together with white wine vinegar, olive oil, prepared horseradish, honey, and salt.

2. Spread each toast with 1 oz ricotta, then spoon salad on top.

*We used country bread but feel free to use your favorite loaf or any leftover pumpernickel you might have this week.

PER SERVING: 131 cal, 4 g pro, 17 g carb, 2 g fiber, 3.5 g sugars (2 g added sugars), 5.5 g fat (1.5 g sat fat), 4 mg chol, 392 mg sodium

CHOPPED EGG SALAD TOAST

No mayo? No problem. This punchy egg salad uses Greek yogurt for creamy richness that comes with a protein boost.

ACTIVE 10 MIN.   TOTAL 10 MIN.   SERVES 4

- 3 Tbsp plain Greek yogurt
- ½ tsp grated lemon zest
- 1 Tbsp lemon juice
- ¼ tsp salt
- ¼ tsp pepper, plus more for serving
- 4 large hard-boiled eggs, peeled and roughly chopped
- ¼ small red onion, finely chopped
- 1 heaping Tbsp capers, chopped
- 1 Tbsp chopped dill, plus more for serving
- 4 pieces pumpernickel toast

1 In bowl, whisk together Greek yogurt, zest, lemon juice, and salt and pepper.

2 Gently mix in eggs. Fold in red onion, capers, and dill.

3 Divide among pumpernickel slices and sprinkle with additional dill and cracked pepper.

PER SERVING: 173 cal, 10 g pro, 17 g carb, 2 g fiber, 1.5 g sugars (0 g added sugars), 7 g fat (2 g sat fat), 188 mg chol, 427 mg sodium

SALMON SALAD WITH GREEN GODDESS DRESSING

Salmon scores major anti-inflammatory points for being high in protein and rich in omega-3s. The dark leafy greens and sweet red tomatoes are antioxidant heavyweights.

ACTIVE 40 MIN.   **TOTAL 40 MIN.**   **SERVES 4**

Kosher salt and pepper

1 8-oz green beans, trimmed

1 lb small new potatoes

1 Tbsp olive oil

1 1¼ lbs center-cut salmon fillet, about 1 in. thick, cut into 2 pieces

½ cup plain yogurt (not Greek)

¼ fresh lemon juice

¼ cup flat-leaf parsley, plus more for serving

¼ cup fresh dill, plus more for serving

¼ cup chopped fresh chives, plus more for serving

1 Tbsp capers, drained

1 ripe avocado, halved

1 5-oz pkg. mixed greens

1 12-oz pkg. mixed-color grape or cherry tomatoes, halved

4 medium-boiled (jammy) eggs, halved

PER SERVING: 489 cal, 42 g pro, 36 g carb, 8 g fiber, 5 g sugars (0 g added sugars), 20 g fat (5 g sat fat), 255 mg chol, 776 mg sodium

1 Bring a pot of water to a boil and fill a bowl with ice water. Add 2 tsp salt, then green beans, and cook until just tender, 2 to 4 min. Transfer to ice water.

2 Add potatoes to pot and simmer until just tender, 8 to 10 min. Drain and run under cold water to cool, then pat dry and cut in half.

3 Meanwhile, in a large skillet over medium-high heat, add oil. Season salmon with ½ tsp each salt and pepper and cook until golden brown and just opaque throughout, 6 to 9 min. per side. Transfer salmon to plate and, using fork, flake into pieces, discarding skin.

4 In blender, puree yogurt, lemon juice, herbs, capers, ½ avocado, 2 Tbsp water, and a pinch each of salt and pepper until smooth.

5 Toss greens with ¼ cup dressing and slice remaining ½ avocado, then divide among plates along with potatoes, green beans, salmon, tomatoes, and eggs. Top with additional herbs if desired and serve with remaining dressing.

TURKEY AND GREENS SOUP

A handful of greens instantly ups this soup's inflammation-fighting power. Creamy white beans offer a double dose of protein and fiber too.

ACTIVE 10 MIN.   TOTAL 25 MIN.   SERVES 4

- 1 Tbsp olive oil
- 1 Tbsp finely chopped fresh rosemary
- 1 small onion, diced
- 2 cups chopped kale
- 1 qt low-sodium chicken broth
- 2½ cups shredded cooked turkey
- 1 15.5-oz can white beans, rinsed and drained

   Kosher salt and pepper

1. In a medium pot, heat oil over medium-high heat. Add rosemary and onion and cook until tender and fragrant, 5 min.

2. Add kale and cook until wilted, 2 min.

3. Stir in broth, turkey, and beans and bring to a simmer. Cook until heated through, 3 min. Season with salt and pepper.

PER SERVING: 291 cal, 38 g pro, 22 g carb, 4 g fiber, 2 g sugars (0 g added sugars), 6 g fat (1 g sat fat), 88 mg chol, 375 mg sodium

CHILI WITH WHEAT BERRIES AND BEANS

This plant-based take on chili is just as satisfying as its meaty counterpart, thanks to smoky fire-roasted tomatoes and stick-to-your-ribs beans and wheat berries.

ACTIVE 20 MIN.   **TOTAL 6 HR. 20 MIN.**   **SERVES 4**

- 1 28-oz can fire-roasted crushed tomatoes
- 1 14.5-oz can no-salt-added diced tomatoes
- 1 Tbsp chili powder
- 2 tsp ground cumin
- 1 tsp ground coriander
- 3 cloves garlic, pressed
- 2 large poblano peppers, cut into ¼-in. pieces
- 1 onion, chopped
- ¾ cup wheat berries
    Kosher salt and pepper
- ½ bunch cilantro
- 2 15.5-oz cans low-sodium beans (1 red kidney, 1 black), rinsed
    Sliced jalapeño and lime wedges, for serving

1. In a slow cooker, combine tomatoes and their juices, chili powder, cumin, coriander, and ¾ cup water.

2. Stir in garlic, poblano peppers, onion, wheat berries, and ½ tsp each salt and pepper. Reserve 1 cup cilantro leaves, then tie remaining together with kitchen twine and add to slow cooker. Cover and cook until wheat berries are tender but still chewy, 5 to 6 hr. on High (or 7 to 8 hr. on Low).

3. Ten min. before serving, remove and discard cilantro bundle and gently stir in beans. Divide among bowls and top with reserved cilantro and jalapeño slices, if desired. Serve with lime wedges.

PER SERVING: 423 cal, 22 g pro, 83 g carb, 23 g fiber, 12.5 g sugars (0 g added sugars), 1.5 g fat (0 g sat fat), 0 mg chol, 981 mg sodium

STRIPED BASS WITH RADISH SALSA VERDE

An herby green salsa gives seafood major gusto with minimal effort on your part. Plus, those aromatic greens are loaded with antioxidant power.

ACTIVE 35 MIN.   **TOTAL 40 MIN.**   **SERVES 4**

1   small clove garlic, pressed

1   Tbsp anchovy paste or 3 anchovy fillets, finely chopped

½   small red onion, finely chopped

1   Tbsp red wine vinegar

½   cup plus 1 Tbsp olive oil, divided

1   bunch radishes, diced, leaves separated and finely chopped

1   cup flat-leaf parsley leaves, finely chopped

1   tsp tarragon leaves, finely chopped

4   6-oz fillets striped bass

Kosher salt and pepper

PER SERVING: 450 cal, 33 g pro, 3 g carb, 1 g fiber, 0.5 g sugars (0 g added sugars), 33.5 g fat (5 g sat fat), 141 mg chol, 640 mg sodium

1 In medium bowl, whisk together garlic, anchovy paste, onion, and vinegar and let sit 5 min.

2 Stir in ½ cup oil, then radishes, radish greens, parsley, and tarragon.

3 Heat remaining Tbsp oil in medium skillet on medium. Pat fish dry and season with ½ tsp each salt and pepper. Cook, skin side down, until skin is crisp and golden brown, about 6 min. Flip and cook until fish is just opaque throughout, 2 to 4 min. more. Serve topped with radish salsa verde.

ANTI-INFLAMMATORY DIET

HERB-POUNDED CHICKEN WITH ARUGULA

Fresh herbs like rosemary and thyme elevate a basic chicken breast in more ways than taste: They pack big flavor plus loads of inflammation-curbing polyphenols.

ACTIVE 5 MIN.   TOTAL 30 MIN.   SERVES 2

2   (6 to 8 oz each) boneless, skinless chicken breasts

3   Tbsp extra virgin olive oil, divided

1   small lemon, zested, plus wedges for serving

2   tsp chopped fresh thyme

1   tsp chopped fresh rosemary

1   small clove garlic, chopped

¼   tsp crushed red pepper flakes
     Kosher salt

2   cups arugula

¼   red onion, thinly sliced

1   tsp balsamic vinegar

PER SERVING: 401 cal, 37 g pro, 4 g carb, 1 g fiber, 2 g sugars (0 g added sugars), 22 g fat (4 g sat fat), 110 mg chol, 349 mg sodium

1. Starting at the thicker side, make a lengthwise cut into the side of the chicken breasts about two-thirds of the way in. Fold the breasts open like a book.

2. In a bowl, mix 1 Tbsp of the oil, lemon zest, thyme, rosemary, garlic, crushed red pepper flakes, and a big pinch of salt. Rub this mixture all over the chicken. Place each chicken breast between two pieces of plastic wrap and use a meat mallet (or bottom of a heavy pan) to pound the breasts to a ¼-in. thickness.

3. In a large skillet over medium-high heat, heat 1 Tbsp olive oil. Add a chicken breast and sear on both sides, about 3 min. each. Transfer to a plate and repeat with the other breast.

4. In a medium bowl, toss the arugula, onion, and balsamic vinegar with the remaining 1 Tbsp olive oil. Squeeze a wedge of lemon over the chicken and serve with the arugula salad.

SLOW COOKER PORK POZOLE VERDE

Red meats like pork can fit into an anti-inflammatory diet, in moderation. Just pair them with high-fiber ingredients like veggies and avocado.

ACTIVE 15 MIN.   TOTAL 5 HR. 15 MIN. on High   SERVES 4 TO 6
(8 HR. 15 MIN. on Low)

12	oz beer
1	Tbsp low-sodium chicken bouillon base (we used Better Than Bouillon)
2	tsp ground cumin
	Kosher salt and pepper
12	oz tomatillos, cut into ½-in. pieces
4	cloves garlic, finely chopped
1	onion, finely chopped
1	4-oz can roasted diced green chiles, drained
1	lb boneless pork butt or shoulder, very well trimmed, cut into 4-in. pieces
1	cup fresh cilantro, plus more for serving
1	28-oz can hominy, rinsed
¼	cup fresh lime juice
	Avocado for serving
	Radishes for serving

1. In 5- to 6-qt slow cooker, combine beer, bouillon base, cumin, 2 cups water, ¼ tsp salt, and ½ tsp pepper.

2. Add tomatillos, garlic, onion, chiles, pork, and cilantro and mix to combine. Cook, covered, until pork is tender and easily pulled apart, 5 to 6 hr. on High or 7 to 8 hr. on Low.

3. Remove and discard cilantro; then, using 2 forks, break pork into smaller pieces. Add hominy and cook, covered, until tender, 3 to 4 min. Stir in lime juice and serve with cilantro, avocado, and radishes if desired.

PER SERVING: 293 cal, 23 g pro, 34 g carb, 9 g fiber, 4.5 g sugars (0 g added sugars), 7.5 g fat (2 g sat fat), 54 mg chol, 803 mg sodium

SEARED SALMON WITH ROASTED CAULIFLOWER

Eating salmon once or twice a week makes it easy to get your recommended amount of omega-3s, especially when you lean on simple, flavorful recipes like this one.

ACTIVE 10 MIN.   TOTAL 25 MIN.   SERVES 4

1½ lbs cauliflower florets (from 1 large head cauliflower)

4 Tbsp olive oil, divided

¼ tsp salt

¼ tsp pepper

4 6-oz pieces salmon

2 cloves chopped garlic

1 Tbsp capers

½ cup parsley leaves

PER SERVING: 305 cal, 36 g pro, 5 g carb, 2 g fiber, 1 g sugars (0g added sugars), 15.5 g fat (3 g sat fat), 80 mg chol, 400 mg sodium

1. Heat oven to 450°F. On a baking sheet, toss cauliflower florets with 2 Tbsp olive oil and salt and pepper. Roast until tender, about 15 min., then increase heat and broil until golden brown.

2. In a large skillet, heat the remaining oil on medium-high. Season the salmon with salt and pepper, then cook for 3 min. Flip salmon, add the garlic and capers to the skillet, and cook until fish is opaque.

3. Transfer salmon to plates. Toss cauliflower with capers, garlic, and parsley leaves; serve with salmon.

COCONUT TRUFFLES

You can feel good about these rich, fudgy confections: The polyphenols in dark chocolate are teeming with antioxidant and anti-inflammatory activity.

ACTIVE 25 MIN.   TOTAL 1 HR. 20 MIN.   SERVES 4

20 oz dark chocolate (72% cacao or higher), very finely chopped, divided

¾ cup coconut milk (well stirred)

Toasted coconut flakes, for decorating

PER SERVING: 125 cal, 2 g pro, 9 g carb, 2 g fiber, 4.5 g sugars (4.5 g added sugars), 9.5 g fat (5.5 g sat fat), 1 mg chol, 5 mg sodium

1 In a medium bowl, place half of chocolate. In a small pan, heat coconut milk until hot to the touch, then pour over chocolate. Cover bowl loosely with a towel and let stand 5 min., then stir until chocolate is melted and smooth.

2 Chill bowl until chocolate is firm enough to scoop but not rock hard, about 30 min. Scoop and roll Tbsp-size balls onto 1 piece of parchment paper; refrigerate.

3 Meanwhile, in a medium bowl, microwave remaining chocolate on High in 30-second increments, stirring frequently until melted and smooth.

4 Working 1 at a time, dip balls in chocolate, then sprinkle with toasted coconut flakes, if desired.

ROASTED APPLES WITH GREEK YOGURT

Greek yogurt delivers a creamy contrast to sweet baked apples, while delivering plenty of protein to keep your blood sugar levels nice and steady.

ACTIVE 15 MIN.   **TOTAL 15 MIN.**   **SERVES 2**

1   Tbsp olive oil

2   apples (halved and cored)

4   sprigs thyme

2   Tbsp vanilla Greek yogurt*

*Feel free to use any leftover plain Greek yogurt you might have this week if you don't want to buy vanilla.

1 **Heat oven to 425°F.**

2 **Coat a small rimmed baking sheet with olive oil. On pan place apples, cut sides down, sprinkle with thyme, and roast until tender, 15 min.**

3 **Place apple halves in bowls, cut side up, and top with dollops of Greek yogurt. Spoon any pan juices on top.**

PER SERVING: 153 cal, 2 g pro, 27 g carb, 4 g fiber, 20 g sugars (1 g added sugars), 5.5 g fat (1 g sat fat), 2 mg chol, 8 mg sodium

APPLE OATMEAL MUFFINS

Pulverized oats take the place of white flour in these lightly sweetened muffins. The result? More fiber bang for your buck at breakfast time.

ACTIVE 20 MIN.   TOTAL 40 MIN.   MAKES 12 MUFFINS

- 2½ cups old-fashioned oats
- ½ tsp grated nutmeg
- ½ tsp ground cinnamon
- ½ tsp kosher salt
- ½ tsp baking powder
- 1 cup pecans, roughly chopped, divided
- ¼ cup olive oil
- ⅓ cup honey, warmed
- 2 large eggs
- 1 tsp pure vanilla extract
- ¾ cup unsweetened almond milk
- 2 Granny Smith apples, peeled and finely diced (2 cups total)

PER SERVING: 225 cal, 4 g pro, 24 g carb, 3 g fiber, 11 g sugars (7.5 g added sugars), 13.5 g fat (1.5 g sat fat), 31 mg chol, 125 mg sodium

1. Heat oven to 375°F. Line a 12-cup muffin pan with cupcake liners and lightly coat with cooking spray.

2. In a food processor, pulse 1 cup oats until very fine (should resemble coarsely milled flour); place in a large bowl. Whisk in nutmeg, cinnamon, salt, and baking powder. Stir in half of pecans.

3. In a medium bowl, whisk together oil and honey, then whisk in eggs, vanilla, and almond milk. Add wet ingredients to dry ones and mix to combine, then fold in apples and remaining 1½ cups oats.

4. Divide batter among liners (about a heaping ¼ cup each) and top with remaining pecans. Bake until tops no longer look shiny, 20 to 25 min.

MASON JAR SCRAMBLE

Here's a protein- and veggie-packed meal that works for busy mornings. The eggs come together in a minute and are cooked in a mason jar for on-the-go eating.

ACTIVE 10 MIN.   TOTAL 10 MIN.   SERVES 2

- 4 large eggs
- 2 Tbsp milk
  Kosher salt and pepper
- ½ cup baby spinach
- 6 grape tomatoes, quartered
- 4 small basil leaves, torn

PER SERVING: 155 cal, 13 g pro, 2 g carb, 0 g fiber, 1 g sugars (0 g added sugars), 10 g fat (3.5 g sat fat), 374 mg chol, 275 mg sodium

1. Between two 10- to 12-oz jars, divide eggs, milk, and pinch each salt and pepper. Screw lids on tightly and shake until well mixed, about 20 sec. Divide baby spinach between the two jars and shake again.

2. Remove lids and microwave jars 60 sec., then in 15-sec. intervals until just set.

3. Top with grape tomatoes and basil leaves.

ROASTED CHICKPEAS

These crunchy, crispy chickpeas are an ideal alternative to highly processed savory snacks, like potato chips.

ACTIVE 5 MIN.   TOTAL 5 MIN.   SERVES 2

2 15-oz cans chickpeas
2 Tbsp extra virgin olive oil
¼ tsp salt
¼ tsp pepper

PER SERVING: 110 cal, 4 g pro, 13 g carb, 4 g fiber, 5 g sugar (0 g added sugars), 5 g fat (0.5 g sat fat), 0 mg chol, 480 mg sodium

1 Heat oven to 425°F. Rinse and drain chickpeas; pat very dry with paper towels, discarding any loose skins.

2 On large rimmed baking sheet, toss with olive oil, salt, and pepper. Roast for 30 min. until crisp, shaking occasionally. Remove from oven and transfer to bowl. Chickpeas will continue to crisp as they cool.

TOMATO TOASTS WITH MINT YOGURT AND SUMAC VINAIGRETTE

Tomatoes are a top source of the carotenoid lycopene, an inflammation fighter whose absorption gets a boost from healthy fats like olive oil.

ACTIVE 10 MIN.   **TOTAL 10 MIN.**   **SERVES 4**

½ cup plain Greek yogurt

1 scallion, finely chopped

¼ cup mint, chopped

2 tsp grated lemon zest

2 Tbsp olive oil

1 tsp lemon juice

¼ tsp cumin seed

¼ tsp ground sumac

¼ tsp coarsely cracked pepper

¼ tsp kosher salt

4 pieces toasted bread

3 medium heirloom tomatoes, sliced

PER SERVING: 182 cal, 8 g pro, 17 g carb, 4 g fiber, 5.5 g sugars (0 g added sugars), 10 g fat (2 g sat fat), 4 mg chol, 243 mg sodium

1. In a bowl, combine plain Greek yogurt, scallion, mint, and grated lemon zest.

2. In second bowl, whisk together olive oil, lemon juice, cumin seed, ground sumac, coarsely cracked pepper, and kosher salt.

3. Spread yogurt mixture on toast, top with heirloom tomatoes, and spoon vinaigrette on top. Sprinkle with additional chopped scallion if desired.

TEMPEH LETTUCE WRAPS

Swapping meaty tempeh for the usual ground beef gives you an extra shot of fiber and polyphenols, while also cutting out the saturated fat.

ACTIVE 20 MIN.   TOTAL 20 MIN.   SERVES 4

1 cup quinoa

1 small zucchini

1 small onion, sliced

1 cup grape tomatoes

1 Tbsp olive oil

   Kosher salt and pepper

8 oz roasted tempeh, cut into pieces

1 cup shredded red cabbage

¾ head Boston lettuce

   Mint leaves for serving

½ cup plain Greek yogurt, for serving

   Lime wedges for serving

PER SERVING: 348 cal, 22 g pro, 42 g carb, 5 g fiber, 5 g sugars (0 g added sugars), 13 g fat (3 g sat fat), 2 mg chol, 157 mg sodium

1 Heat oven to 450°F. Cook quinoa per pkg. directions.

2 Halve zucchini lengthwise and cut into 1-in. pieces. On rimmed baking sheet, toss zucchini, onion, and grape tomatoes with olive oil, and season with ¼ tsp each kosher salt and pepper. Roast until just tender, 10 to 12 min.; transfer to bowl.

3 Fluff quinoa and add to bowl with vegetables along with tempeh and red cabbage; toss to combine.

4 Separate leaves from lettuce head. Fill lettuce leaves with quinoa mixture and top with mint leaves. Dollop with Greek yogurt and serve with lime wedges.

SEARED SALMON WITH SPICED SWEET POTATOES

With 32 grams of protein and just 389 calories, this light lunch will leave you satisfied and energized all afternoon.

ACTIVE 15 MIN.   TOTAL 35 MIN.   SERVES 4

- 2 lbs sweet potatoes, cut into 2-in. pieces
- 3 Tbsp extra virgin olive oil, divided
- 1 Tbsp coriander seeds, crushed
- 2 Tbsp chopped fresh dill
- 1 red chile, thinly sliced
-    Kosher salt
-    Pepper
- 2 Tbsp fresh clementine juice
- 1 tsp honey
- 1 tsp grated peeled fresh ginger
- 1 tsp white wine vinegar
- 1 ¼ lb skinless salmon fillet, cut into 4 portions
-    Cilantro, for serving

PER SERVING: 389 cal, 32 g pro, 204 g carb, 38 g fiber, 52 g sugars (8 g added sugars), 70.5 g fat (18.5 g sat fat), 453 mg chol, 2,791 mg sodium

1. Heat oven to 425°F. On rimmed baking sheet, toss sweet potatoes with 1 Tbsp oil, then with crushed coriander, chile, and ½ tsp each salt and pepper. Roast until golden brown and tender, 20 to 25 min.

2. Meanwhile, in bowl, whisk together clementine juice, honey, ginger, vinegar, and 1 Tbsp oil.

3. Heat remaining Tbsp oil in large skillet on medium-high. Season salmon with ½ tsp each salt and pepper and cook until golden brown and just opaque throughout, 5 to 6 min. per side. Serve with sweet potatoes, drizzle with vinaigrette, and sprinkle with cilantro if desired.

WILD SALMON SALAD

Healthy fats and fiber are the name of the game in this hearty salad, which combines buttery salmon, creamy avocado, crunchy almonds, and tender baby greens.

ACTIVE 15 MIN.   TOTAL 15 MIN.   SERVES 2

- 2 **4-oz pieces skinless wild Alaskan salmon fillet**
  Kosher salt and pepper
- 1 **Tbsp balsamic vinegar**
- 2 **tsp olive oil**
- 1 **cup grape tomatoes, halved**
- 1 **scallion, thinly sliced**
- 3 **cups mixed baby greens**
- ½ **avocado, sliced**
- ¼ **cup slivered almonds, toasted**

① Heat oven to 375°F. On a rimmed baking sheet, season salmon with ¼ tsp each salt and pepper, and roast until opaque throughout, 10 to 12 min.

② Meanwhile, in a large bowl, whisk together vinegar, oil, and a pinch each of salt and pepper. Toss with tomatoes, then fold in scallions followed by greens.

③ Serve with salmon and avocado and sprinkle with almonds.

PER SERVING: 340 cal, 28 g pro, 13 g carb, 7 g fiber, 4.5 g sugars (0 g added sugars), 20.5 g fat (3 g sat fat), 53 mg chol, 350 mg sodium

GREEK CHICKPEA TACOS

You won't miss the meat in these gyro-inspired tacos—especially not with this hearty filling of lemony mashed chickpeas, creamy Greek yogurt, and briny olives.

ACTIVE 10 MIN.   TOTAL 20 MIN.   SERVES 4

- 1 **15-oz can unsalted chickpeas, drained and rinsed**
- 2 **Tbsp fresh lemon juice, divided**
- 2 **Tbsp olive oil**
- 1 **tsp dried oregano**
- 4 **whole-wheat pitas (6-in. diameter), warmed**
- 2 **cups mixed spring greens**
- 1 **large tomato, diced**
- ½ **small red onion, thinly sliced**
- ¼ **cup pitted kalamata olives, sliced**
- ½ **seedless cucumber, peeled and grated (reserve and dice extra cucumber for garnish if desired)**
- 1 **cup plain Greek yogurt**
- 2 **Tbsp chopped mint, plus leaves for garnish**
- 1 **clove garlic, minced**
   Kosher salt

1. In a medium bowl, mash chickpeas with 1 Tbsp lemon juice, olive oil, and oregano. Spread ¼ of mixture on each pita. Top with greens, tomato, onion, and olives.

2. In a medium bowl, combine cucumber, yogurt, mint, remaining 1 Tbsp lemon juice, garlic, and a pinch of salt. Drizzle over taco fillings. Top with more mint and diced cucumber if desired.

PER SERVING: 429 cal, 17 g pro, 58 g carb, 10 g fiber, 6 g sugars (0 g added sugars), 16.5 g fat (3.5 g sat fat), 8 mg chol, 696 mg sodium

COLORFUL QUINOA BOWLS

Tofu, quinoa, ginger, and a rainbow of assorted veggies come together in an Asian-inspired bowl that gives inflammation the boot.

ACTIVE 20 MIN.   TOTAL 50 MIN.   SERVES 4

1¼ cup quinoa

6 Tbsp rice vinegar

¼ cup white miso

2 tsp grated fresh ginger

¼ cup plus 1½ Tbsp extra virgin olive oil, divided

14 oz firm tofu, pressed dry and cut into 1-in. cubes

1 large sweet potato, cut into 1-in. pieces

2 medium beets, cut into ½-in. wedges

¼ cup small red cabbage, very thinly sliced

1 cup snow peas, halved

1 cup cilantro

2 scallions, thinly sliced

1 Tbsp sesame seeds

PER SERVING: 544 cal, 21 g pro, 66 g carb, 12 g fiber, 23 g fat (2 g sat fat), 13g sugars (0 g added sugars), 0 mg chol, 608 mg sodium

1 Heat oven to 425°F. Cook quinoa per pkg. directions.

2 In a bowl, whisk vinegar, miso, ginger, and ¼ oil.

3 Brush 1 rimmed baking sheet with ½ Tbsp oil. In bowl, toss tofu with ¼ cup dressing to coat and place on oiled pan.

4 On second pan, toss sweet potato and beets with remaining Tbsp oil and ¼ tsp each salt and pepper. Transfer both pans to oven and roast until vegetables are golden brown and tender and tofu is golden brown and crisp, 25 to 30 min.

5 Divide quinoa among 4 bowls. Top with tofu, roasted vegetables, cabbage, peas, cilantro, scallions, sesame seeds, drizzle with remaining dressing.

RAINBOW CHICKEN SLAW

The vibrant colors (orange! purple! green!) let you know
that this sweet, crunchy slaw is all about the antioxidants.

ACTIVE 20 MIN.   TOTAL 1 HR. 20 MIN.   SERVES 2

½ cup low-fat buttermilk

4 tsp fresh lemon juice

2 small cloves garlic, finely grated

2 tsp honey mustard

   Kosher salt and pepper

1½ cups shredded cooked chicken

1 cup thinly sliced red cabbage

2 small carrots, coarsely grated

2 small rainbow or Chioggia
   beets, scrubbed and very thinly
   sliced

1 avocado, sliced

½ cup snow pea shoots

PER SERVING: 460 cal, 32 g pro, 33g
carb, 12 g fiber, 16.5 g sugars (1.5 g
added sugars), 24.5 g fat (4.5 g sat fat),
78 mg chol, 740 mg sodium

1 In a bowl, whisk together buttermilk, lemon
juice, garlic, honey mustard, and ¼ tsp pepper.
Transfer half of dressing to a small bowl and
set aside. Add chicken to remaining bowl of
dressing and toss to coat.

2 Arrange cabbage, carrots, beets, avocado,
and pea shoots on 2 large plates and season
with salt and pepper. Top with chicken
and drizzle with remaining dressing, tossing
before eating.

PISTACHIO-CRUSTED FISH AND SPINACH QUINOA

Finely chopped pistachios and whole-wheat panko take the place of white-flour breadcrumbs for a rich, buttery coating that's also full of fiber.

ACTIVE 20 MIN.   TOTAL 20 MIN.   SERVES 4

¾ cup quinoa

4 6-oz pieces firm skinless white fish (such as cod or tilapia)

¾ tsp salt, divided

½ tsp pepper, divided

1 Tbsp plain Greek yogurt

¼ cup whole-wheat panko

¼ cup unsalted shelled pistachios, finely chopped

2 Tbsp olive oil, divided

4 cups baby spinach

2 Tbsp lemon juice

PER SERVING: 377 cal, 35 g pro, 29 g carb, 4 g fiber, 2 g sugars (0 g added sugars), 14 g fat (2 g sat fat), 65 mg chol, 370 mg sodium

1 Cook quinoa per pkg. directions.

2 Season white fish with ½ tsp salt and ¼ tsp pepper, then brush yogurt on each.

3 Mix whole-wheat panko and unsalted shelled pistachios with 1 Tbsp olive oil; sprinkle over fish, pressing gently to adhere. Bake on nonstick foil-lined rimmed baking sheet at 375°F until opaque throughout, 12 to 15 min.

4 Fluff quinoa, then add baby spinach, lemon juice, 1 Tbsp olive oil, and ¼ tsp each salt and pepper; toss to combine and serve with fish.

PORK AND PEACH KEBABS WITH GRILLED GREEN BEANS

This juicy dish is a genius way to get both fruits and vegetables on your plate at dinnertime.

ACTIVE 30 MIN.   TOTAL 30 MIN.   SERVES 4

¼ cup peach jam

1 Tbsp rice vinegar

2 Tbsp grated fresh ginger, divided

1 lb green beans, trimmed

2 Tbsp olive oil, divided
   Kosher salt and pepper

1¼ lb pork loin, trimmed, cut into 1-in. chunks

2 peaches, cut into ¾-in. thick wedges

1 red onion, cut into ½-in. thick wedges

PER SERVING: 380 cal, 29 g pro, 31 g carb, 4 g fiber, 22 g sugars (12 g added sugars), 16 g fat (4 g sat fat), 79 mg chol, 425 mg sodium

1 Heat grill on medium. In a small bowl, combine jam, vinegar, and 1 Tbsp ginger. In a large bowl, toss green beans with 1 Tbsp oil, then remaining Tbsp ginger and ¼ tsp each salt and pepper.

2 Thread pork, peaches, and red onion onto 8 skewers. Brush with remaining Tbsp olive oil and season with ½ tsp each salt and pepper. Grill, turning occasionally, 5 min. Continue grilling and glazing with sauce until pork is just cooked through, 2 to 4 min. more.

3 During the last 5 min. of cooking, grill green beans, turning occasionally, until tender, 3 to 5 min. Serve green beans with kebabs.

PEACHES WITH HONEY AND PISTACHIOS

Grilling peaches brings out their natural sweetness without the need for lots of added sugar. They get a protein hit from the Greek yogurt and pistachios too.

ACTIVE 10 MIN.   TOTAL 10 MIN.   SERVES 4

- 4 peaches, halved
- ½ cup plain Greek yogurt
- ½ tsp grated orange zest
- 2 Tbsp honey
- ¼ cup shelled unsalted pistachios, chopped
- Mint leaves, for serving

PER SERVING: 166 cal, 6 g pro, 27 g carb, 3 g fiber, 22.5 g sugars (8.5 g added sugars), 5.5 g fat (1 g sat fat), 4 mg chol, 12 mg sodium

1. Heat grill to medium. Grill peaches, cut sides down, until slightly charred and caramelized, 1 to 2 min. Turn and cook, covered, 2 min. more.

2. In a bowl, combine yogurt and orange zest. Transfer peaches to plates and spoon yogurt on top, then drizzle with honey and sprinkle with pistachios and mint leaves.

AVOCADO MOUSSE

Creamy avocado and a touch of almond milk are used as milk and egg imposters in this easy blender mousse. (But you'd never know it by the taste!)

ACTIVE 5 MIN.   **TOTAL 5 MIN.**   **SERVES 2**

1   large, ripe avocado

¼   cup Dutch process cocoa

3   Tbsp unsweetened almond milk

1   Tbsp honey

1   pure vanilla extract

    Salt

    Shaved chocolate, for serving

 In mini food processor, puree avocado, cocoa, almond milk, honey, vanilla extract, and pinch of salt. Chill if desired.

 Divide between 2 small glasses and serve with shaved chocolate.

PER SERVING: 304 cal, 5 g pro, 33 g carb, 12 g fiber, 18 g sugars (17.5 g added sugars), 21 g fat (2.5 g sat fat), 0 mg chol, 88 mg sodium

BLOOD ORANGE AND OLIVE OIL SHORTBREAD

Heart-healthy olive oil is the secret to these butter-free shortbreads, which are rich, tender, and practically free of saturated fat.

ACTIVE 15 MIN.   TOTAL 30 MIN. PLUS COOLING   SERVES 48

- 3 cups all-purpose flour
- ½ tsp kosher salt
- 2¼ cups confectioners' sugar, divided
- 1 cup extra virgin olive oil
- 2 tsp pure vanilla extract
- 2 Tbsp blood orange juice

PER SERVING: 95 cal, 1 g pro, 12 g carb, 0 g fiber, 5.5 g sugars (5.5 g added sugars), 4.5 g fat (0.5 g sat fat), 0 mg chol, 20 mg sodium

1. Heat oven to 350°F. In a bowl, whisk together flour, salt, and 1 cup confectioners' sugar. Add oil and vanilla and mix to combine.

2. Transfer dough to 1 piece of parchment paper and cover with another. Using a rolling pin, roll to ¼ in. thick. Slide onto a baking sheet, remove top piece of parchment, and bake until edges are light golden brown, about 15 min. With shortbread still on baking sheet, immediately cut into 1- by 2-in. rectangles, but do not move or handle. Let cool completely, about 30 min.

3. When cookies are cool, whisk together blood orange juice and remaining 1¼ cups confectioners' sugar. Dip cooled cookies into glaze and place on parchment to dry. Store covered at room temperature.

BANANA AND ALMOND BUTTER PANCAKES

Swapping white flour for protein-rich almond butter and high-fiber bananas means you stay full—and your blood sugar stays steady!—all morning.

ACTIVE 15 MIN.   TOTAL 50 MIN.   SERVES 4

2 very ripe bananas, plus sliced bananas for serving

6 Tbsp smooth almond butter

3 large eggs

   Honey, for serving

PER SERVING: (3 pancakes) 350 cal, 11 g pro, 44 g carb, 5 g fiber, 30 g sugar (17 g added sugars), 17 g fat (2 g sat fat), 140 mg chol, 55 mg sodium

1 In a medium bowl, mash bananas with the almond butter until smooth. Using a fork, whisk in the eggs.

2 Heat a nonstick skillet on medium-low. Add spoonfuls of the batter (about 3 Tbsp each) to the skillet and cook until bubbles begin to burst around the edges and in the center, 2 to 3 min. Flip and cook 1 min. more, making sure the underside is golden brown.

3 Transfer to a baking sheet, cover loosely with foil and keep warm in a low oven. Repeat with remaining batter. (If your pancakes stick, wipe the skillet with 1 tsp oil before cooking the next batch.) Serve with honey, if desired.

BLUEBERRY AND MIXED NUT PARFAIT

Pair Greek yogurt and nuts for a satisfying breakfast that packs 22 grams of protein. The blueberry sauce adds sweetness and powerful polyphenols like anthocyanins.

ACTIVE 25 MIN.   TOTAL 35 MIN.   SERVES 4

1   cup freeze-dried blueberries
    Flaky sea salt
3   Tbsp walnuts
3   Tbsp almonds
3   Tbsp pecans
3   Tbsp pepitas
1   Tbsp olive oil
1   tsp cinnamon
⅛   tsp cardamom
1   Tbsp orange zest
¼   cup golden raisins
3   cups Greek yogurt

PER SERVING: 415 cal, 22 g pro, 28 g carb, 4 g fiber, 21.5 g sugars (0 g added sugars), 25.5 g fat (6.5 g sat fat), 25 mg chol, 390 mg sodium

1   In a food processor, pulse ½ cup freeze-dried blueberries to form a powder; transfer to a small saucepan. Whisk in 1 cup water and simmer until thickened, about 15 min. Stir in pinch salt; let cool.

2   Heat oven to 400°F. Toss walnuts, almonds, pecans, and pepitas with olive oil, cinnamon, cardamom and ½ tsp flaky sea salt. Roast until toasted, about 6 min., then toss with orange zest, ½ cup (or remainder of package) freeze-dried blueberries, and golden raisins.

3   Make 4 parfaits, layering Greek yogurt (about ¾ cup for each parfait), blueberry sauce (about 1 heaping Tbsp), and nut mixture (heaping ¼ cup).

CURRY-AVOCADO CRISPY EGG TOAST

Curry powder wakes up the flavor of avocado-and-egg toast and brings a shot of antioxidant-rich spices like turmeric, black pepper, and coriander.

ACTIVE 10 MIN. **TOTAL 10 MIN.** **SERVES 2**

½ tsp curry powder

3 Tbsp olive oil, divided

½ large avocado

2 tsp fresh lime juice

Kosher salt and pepper

2 slices whole-grain bread, toasted

2 large eggs

2 Tbsp finely chopped cilantro

PER SERVING: 453 cal, 13 g pro, 24 g carb, 8 g fiber, 3.5 g sugars (0 g added sugars), 34.5 g fat (6 g sat fat), 185 mg chol, 378 mg sodium

1 In a small dry skillet on medium, toast curry powder until fragrant, 1 min. Stir in 2 Tbsp olive oil and set aside.

2 Mash avocado with lime juice and pinch of salt, and spread on toast.

3 In a medium non-stick skillet on medium-high, heat remaining Tbsp oil. Add eggs and cook until whites are golden brown, crisp around edges, and set around yolks, about 2 min. (If edges are dark but whites are not set, remove skillet from heat; cover until whites are cooked, about 10 seconds.) Season with pinch each salt and pepper.

4 Top each slice of avocado toast with egg and chopped cilantro, then drizzle with curry oil.

SPINACH AND CHEESE NAAN PIZZAS AND TOMATO SALAD

Instead of reducing tomatoes into sauce, this recipe serves them fresh alongside your pizza, offering way more vitamin C than their cooked counterparts.

ACTIVE 20 MIN.   **TOTAL 20 MIN.**   **SERVES 2**

- 1 naan, split in half horizontally
- 1 clove garlic, finely grated
- 1½ Tbsp olive oil
- ⅛ tsp red pepper flakes
- ¼ tsp kosher salt
- ½ lb large tomatoes, cut into chunks
- ½ small bunch spinach, thick stems discarded (about 2 cups)
- 1½ oz very thinly sliced provolone, torn
- 1 oz feta, crumbled

PER SERVING: 314 cal, 12 g pro, 23 g carb, 3 g fiber, 2.5 g sugars (0 g added sugars), 19.5 g fat (7.5 g sat fat), 27 mg chol

1 **Place naan, cut sides down, on a foil-lined baking sheet. Bake at 450°F until golden brown and crisp, 5 to 6 min. Flip over so cut sides are facing up.**

2 **Meanwhile, in a bowl, combine garlic, olive oil, red pepper flakes, and salt.**

3 **Transfer ½ Tbsp of oil mixture to a second bowl and toss with tomatoes. Let sit until ready to serve.**

4 **Toss spinach in remaining oil mixture to coat. Divide spinach, provolone, and feta among pitas. Bake until cheese melts, 5 min. Serve hot with tomato salad.**

SHRIMP, AVOCADO, AND EGG CHOPPED SALAD

Who says a salad needs beef or chicken to be satisfying? You'll get 40 grams of protein from this one, thanks to the shrimp and hard-boiled eggs.

ACTIVE 10 MIN.   **TOTAL 15 MIN.**   **SERVES 2**

¼ small red onion, thinly sliced

2 Tbsp fresh lime juice

1 Tbsp olive oil, divided

12 oz peeled and deveined large shrimp

   Kosher salt and pepper

1 cup grape tomatoes, halved

8 cups butter lettuce

½ cup fresh cilantro leaves

½ avocado, diced

2 hard-boiled eggs, cut into pieces

PER SERVING: 365 cal, 40 g pro, 15 g carb, 7 g fiber, 7 g sugars (0 g added sugars), 17 g fat (5 g sat fat), 450 mg chol, 600 mg sodium

1 In a large bowl, toss onion with lime juice and ½ Tbsp oil and let sit for 5 min.

2 In a large skillet on medium-high, heat remaining ½ Tbsp oil. Season shrimp with ¼ tsp each salt and pepper and cook until opaque throughout, 2 to 3 min. per side.

3 Toss tomatoes with onions, then toss with lettuce and cilantro. Divide between bowls and top with shrimp, avocado, and egg.

Refrigerate the soup and pesto separately for up to 3 days. Warm soup in a saucepan on medium until heated through, then serve with pesto.

SPRING MINESTRONE SOUP WITH HOMEMADE PESTO

A pesto made of dill, fennel, olive oil, and cashews gets swirled into this brothy soup. The rich, flavorful result packs tons of anti-inflammatory oomph.

ACTIVE 20 MIN.   TOTAL 20 MIN.   SERVES 6

FOR SOUP

- 2 Tbsp olive oil
- 2 leeks (white and light green parts only, sliced into ¼-in.-thick half-moons)
- 1 small bulb fennel (fronds reserved, bulb cored and cut into ¼-in. pieces)
  Kosher salt and pepper
- 3½ Tbsp low-sodium vegetable base
- 1 lb asparagus, trimmed and cut into ½-in. pieces
- 8 oz green beans, sliced into ¼-in. rounds
- 4 oz sugar snap peas, strings removed and cut into thirds
- 1 15-oz can cannellini beans, rinsed

FOR PESTO

- 1 cup fresh dill
- 1 cup reserved fennel fronds
- ¼ cup cashews
- 2 oz Parmesan, grated
- 2 cloves garlic
- 3 Tbsp fresh lemon juice
- ¼ cup olive oil

1 In a Dutch oven on medium-low, heat oil. Add leeks, fennel, and ¼ tsp kosher salt and cook, covered, stirring occasionally, until just tender, 8 min.

2 Add vegetable base and 8 cups water and bring to a boil, then reduce heat and simmer until pesto is ready.

3 **Make Pesto:** In a blender, puree dill, reserved fennel fronds, cashews, Parmesan, garlic, and lemon juice until smooth. With motor running, slowly add olive oil.

4 To soup, add asparagus, green beans, sugar snap peas, and cannellini beans, and simmer until just tender, 4 min. Serve pesto on soup.

PER SERVING: 323 cal, 13 g pro, 30 g carb, 9 g fiber, 8 g sugars (0 g added sugars), 18.5 g fat (4 g sat fat), 6 mg chol, 517 mg sodium

GREEK CHICKEN TACOS

Move over, beef. These Mediterranean-inspired ground chicken and veggie tacos bring inflammation down instead of ramping it up.

ACTIVE 15 MIN.   **TOTAL 15 MIN.**   **SERVES 4**

- 1 Tbsp olive oil
- 1 lb ground chicken
- 1 tsp dried oregano
- ½ tsp ground black pepper
- 4 whole-wheat pita breads
- 1 tomato, diced
- ½ cucumber, diced
- ½ cup plain Greek yogurt
- 1 Tbsp fresh chopped dill
- 1 tsp fresh lemon zest
- ¼ cup crumbled feta cheese

PER SERVING: 422 cal, 31 g pro, 30 g carb, 6 g fiber, 3 g sugars (3 g added sugars), 17 g fat (5 g saturated fat), 110 mg chol, 469 mg sodium

1. In a large skillet over medium heat, add the oil, chicken, oregano, and black pepper and cook until no longer pink, 5 to 6 min.

2. Meanwhile, warm the pita breads in a toaster oven, oven, or microwave.

3. Divide the chicken mixture among the pita breads (down the middle, so you can fold up the sides and eat them like tacos). Top each with tomato and cucumber.

4. In a small bowl, combine the yogurt, dill, and lemon zest. Drizzle over the tacos and sprinkle with the feta.

HONEY-SPICED SALMON WITH QUINOA

High-protein and omega-3-rich salmon plus fiber-filled quinoa join forces to keep your blood sugar stable for lasting energy.

ACTIVE 20 MIN.   TOTAL 35 MIN.   SERVES 4

1 cup quinoa
2 limes, plus wedges for serving if desired
2 Tbsp oil
1 Tbsp freshly grated ginger
1 Tbsp plus 1 tsp honey
   Kosher salt and pepper
2 scallions, thinly sliced (dark green parts separated)
12 oz red cabbage, cored and finely shredded
1½ lbs skinless salmon fillet, cut into 4 pieces
½ tsp cayenne

PER SERVING: 465 cal, 41 g pro, 38 g carb, 5 g fiber, 6 g sugars (6 g added sugars), 16 g fat (2 g sat fat), 66 mg chol, 460 mg sodium

1 In a medium saucepan over medium heat, add quinoa, and cook, shaking pan occasionally, until lightly toasted, 5 min. Add 2 cups water and immediately cover (it will spatter). Simmer gently, 10 min. Remove from heat, remove lid, cover with a clean towel, and let stand 10 min.; fluff with a fork.

2 Meanwhile, in a large bowl, finely grate zest of 1 lime then squeeze in juice (you'll need 3 Tbsp total). Whisk in oil, ginger, 1 tsp honey, and ¼ tsp each salt and pepper. Stir in white and light-green parts of scallions, then toss with cabbage.

3 Heat the broiler. On a rimmed baking sheet lined with nonstick foil, place the salmon and season with cayenne and ½ tsp salt. Drizzle with remaining 1 Tbsp honey and broil until opaque throughout and browned on top, 5 to 7 min.

4 Fold cooked quinoa into cabbage mixture, then sprinkle with reserved green parts of scallions. Serve with salmon, and lime wedges if desired.

GRILLED YOGURT-MARINATED CHICKEN

A zesty yogurt, ginger, citrus, and spice-filled marinade gives this juicy grilled chicken an edge over basic burgers any day of the week.

ACTIVE 25 MIN.   TOTAL 3 HR. 35 MIN.   SERVES 4

Kosher salt

1 3½- to 4-lbs chicken, backbone removed

1 cup plain yogurt, not Greek

4 large cloves garlic, grated

2 1-in. piece peeled fresh ginger, grated

1 Tbsp grated lime zest

¼ lime juice

2 Tbsp sweet paprika

1½ Tbsp ground coriander

2 tsp red pepper flakes

PER SERVING: 352 cal, 39 g pro, 2 g carb, 1 g fiber, 1 g sugars (0 g added sugars), 20 g fat (5.5 g sat fat), 126 mg chol, 569 mg sodium

1. Season chicken with ½ tsp salt and let sit while you prepare marinade.

2. In a large bowl, whisk together yogurt, garlic, ginger, lime zest and juice, paprika, coriander, cumin, red pepper, and ½ tsp salt; transfer half to small bowl, then cover and refrigerate.

3. Add chicken to a large bowl and coat all over in yogurt mixture. Refrigerate at least 2½ hr. or up to overnight.

4. Heat grill on medium-high. For gas grill, turn off burners on 1 side; if using charcoal, move charcoal to 1 side (this creates an indirect-heat cooking area).

5. Remove chicken from marinade (discard marinade), place skin side down over direct heat, and grill until beginning to char, 2 min. Flip chicken over, transfer to indirect heat side of grill, and cook, covered, 20 min.

6. Brush chicken with some of reserved yogurt mixture, rotate, and continue grilling 15 min. Brush with additional yogurt mixture, rotate, and grill until internal temperature of thigh registers 165°F, 15 to 20 min. more depending on size of bird (if you like more color, you can sear the breast one more time over direct heat before removing it from the grill). Transfer to cutting board and let rest at least 10 min. before cutting into pieces.

GREEN ENVY RICE BOWL

Spicy kimchi livens up these chicken and veggie bowls. Plus, it's chock-full of anti-inflammatory compounds including beta-carotene and vitamin C.

ACTIVE 10 MIN.   TOTAL 40 MIN.   SERVES 4

- 1 lb asparagus, trimmed and chopped
- 1 onion, chopped
- ½ lb Brussels sprouts, trimmed and halved
- ½ lb cremini or button mushrooms, halved (quartered if large)
- 2 tsp olive oil
- 1 tsp ground cumin
- 1 tsp sweet paprika
- 1 tsp garlic powder
- 1 tsp kosher salt
- 2 cups cooked brown rice
- 2 cups diced or shredded leftover cooked or rotisserie chicken (light and/or dark meat)
- 1 cup kimchi, optional
- 1 avocado, sliced
- 4 Tbsp Tahini Garlic Dressing (right)

PER SERVING: 478 cal, 31 g pro, 40 g carb, 9 g fiber, 5 g sugars (0 g added sugars), 23 g fat (3.5 g saturated fat), 53 g chol, 623 mg sodium

1. Heat the oven to 425°F.

2. On a baking sheet, combine the asparagus, onion, Brussels sprouts, and mushrooms with the olive oil, cumin, paprika, garlic powder, and salt. Spread out on the baking sheet, tossing once, and roast until the veggies are slightly charred, 25 to 30 min.

3. Divide the rice among 4 bowls. Top each with ½ cup chicken, ¼ cup kimchi (if using), and ¼ avocado. Drizzle with 1 Tbsp Tahini Garlic Dressing each.

Tahini Garlic Dressing

ACTIVE 5 MIN.   TOTAL 5 MIN.   SERVES 12

- ¼ cup tahini
- ¼ cup olive oil
- ¼ cup apple cider vinegar
- 2 or 3 cloves garlic, minced
- 1 tsp miso
- ¼ tsp salt
- ¼ tsp ground black pepper

1. In a glass jar, combine tahini, olive oil, and apple cider vinegar. Add garlic, miso, salt, and pepper. Thin with water to desired consistency. Store in the fridge for up to 1 week. Makes ¾ cup.

* Note: If you don't have miso, sub in ½ teaspoon sea salt.

PER SERVING: 74 cal, 1 g pro, 2 g carb, 0 g fiber, 0 g sugars (0 g added sugars), 7 g fat (1 g sat fat), 0 mg chol, 68 mg sodium

DARK CHOCOLATE POWER BARK

Antioxidant-rich dark chocolate and dried cherries plus cholesterol-lowering pecans equal one feel-good dessert.

ACTIVE 5 MIN.   TOTAL 5 MIN. PLUS STANDING   SERVES 8 TO 12

14   oz dark chocolate (at least 70% cacao), chopped into small pieces

¾   cup granola (we love Early Bird)

¾   cup dried tart cherries

¼   cup chopped pecans

PER SERVING: 316 cal, 4 g pro, 31 g carb, 5 g fiber, 18 g sugars (13.5 g added sugars), 20.5 g fat (10 g sat fat), 1 mg chol, 35 mg sodium

1. Line large baking sheet with foil or parchment.

2. In a large bowl place chocolate. Microwave in 20-second intervals, stirring after each, until completely melted (about 2 min. total).

3. Pour melted chocolate onto prepared baking sheet and smooth with offset spatula to approximately ⅛-in. thickness. Evenly sprinkle granola, cherries, and pecans over chocolate.

4. Let bark sit until firm, about 3 hr. at room temp or about 30 min. in refrigerator. Peel off foil and break bark into pieces. Refrigerate in airtight container up to 1 week or freeze up to 3 months.

STRAWBERRY-THYME MILLET BOWL

Roasting strawberries in the oven intensifies their natural sugars, nixing the need to douse this hearty porridge in added sweeteners.

ACTIVE 15 MIN.   TOTAL 45 MIN.   SERVES 4

- 1 lb strawberries, hulled and halved
- 4 sprigs fresh thyme, plus more for serving
- 1 Tbsp olive oil
- 1 Tbsp honey
- 1 cup 2% milk, plus more for serving
- 1 cup millet
- 1½ tsp pure vanilla extract
- 2 Tbsp finely chopped unsalted pistachios
- 2 Tbsp hemp seeds

1. Heat oven to 450°F. On rimmed baking sheet, toss strawberries, thyme, oil, and honey. Roast until berries begin to release juices, about 10 min. Remove from oven and discard thyme.

2. Meanwhile, in saucepan, bring milk and 1 cup water to a boil. Stir in millet and vanilla, reduce heat, and simmer, covered, until millet is tender and liquid is absorbed, 25 to 30 min. Serve millet with berries and pan juices, a splash of milk, pistachios, and hemp seeds and thyme.

PER SERVING: 358 cal, 11 g pro, 54 g carb, 7 g fiber, 14.5 g sugars (4.5 g added sugars), 11 g fat (2 g sat fat), 6 mg chol, 37 mg sodium

SUNNY-SIDE-UP EGGS ON GARLICKY GREENS

Piling eggs on top of a tangle of sautéed greens rather than the usual white toast keeps your blood sugar on an even keel all morning.

ACTIVE 10 MIN.   TOTAL 12 MIN.   SERVES 2

4   tsp olive oil, divided
1   tsp minced garlic
3   cups chopped dark leafy greens
    Kosher salt and pepper
2   eggs
    Red pepper flakes, and lemon zest, for topping

PER SERVING: 166 cal, 7 g pro, 3 g carb, 1 g fiber, 14 g fat (3 g sat fat), 1 g sugars (0 g added sugars), 186 mg chol, 320 mg sodium

1. In a small nonstick skillet, heat 2 tsp olive oil. Sauté garlic and greens until wilted, about 3 min.; season with salt and pepper and remove from pan.

2. In same skillet, add remaining 2 tsp oil and fry eggs on medium-high for 4 min.

3. Top greens with fried egg; garnish with red pepper flakes and lemon zest before serving.

VEGGIE-LOADED CHICKPEA WAFFLES

Found: Waffles that don't make you want to take a nap mid-morning (and actually keep you full). Just trade the white flour for protein- and fiber-filled chickpea flour.

ACTIVE 10 MIN.   **TOTAL 15 MIN.**   **MAKES 8**

- ½ cup chickpea flour
- ¼ tsp baking soda
     Kosher salt and pepper
- ½ cup plain 2% Greek yogurt
- 4 large eggs
- 2 scallions, finely chopped
- 1 cup baby spinach, roughly chopped
- ½ small red pepper, cut into thin pieces
- 3 Tbsp grated Pecorino Romano cheese

PER SERVING: 81 cal, 6 g pro, 5 g carb, 1 g fiber, 2 g sugars (0 g added sugars), 4 g fat (1.5 g sat fat), 95 mg chol, 180 mg sodium

1 Heat oven to 200°F. Set a wire rack over a rimmed baking sheet and place in oven. Heat waffle iron per directions.

2 In a large bowl, whisk together chickpea flour, baking soda, and ¼ tsp salt. In a small bowl, whisk together yogurt and eggs. Stir wet ingredients into dry ingredients. Fold in scallions, spinach, red pepper, pecorino, and ¼ tsp pepper.

3 Lightly coat waffle iron with nonstick cooking spray and, in batches, drop ¼ cup batter into each section of iron and cook until golden brown, 4 to 5 min. Transfer to rack in oven and keep warm. Repeat with remaining batter.

SPINACH-CURRY CREPES WITH APPLE, RAISINS, AND CHICKPEAS

Filled with anti-inflammatory heavy hitters like spinach, apples, chickpeas, and curry powder, these Indian-inspired crepes straddle the line between savory and sweet.

ACTIVE 30 MIN.   TOTAL 30 MIN.   SERVES 4

1   large egg
¼   cup cilantro, finely chopped
1¼ cups 1% milk, divided
½   cup + 1Tbsp all-purpose flour, divided
1½ Tbsp canola oil, plus more for pan
    Kosher salt and pepper
1   small onion, finely chopped
1   15.5-oz can chickpeas, rinsed
½   Granny Smith apple, cut into ¼-in. pieces
2   Tbsp golden raisins
1   Tbsp Madras curry powder
1   5-oz pkg. baby spinach
    Lemon wedges, for serving

PER SERVING: 325 cal, 12 g pro, 45 g carb, 8 g fiber, 13 g sugars (0 g added sugars), 10.5 g fat (1.5 g sat fat), 50 mg chol, 475 mg sodium

1 In blender, puree egg, cilantro, ½ cup each of the milk and flour, 1 Tbsp oil, and ¼ tsp each salt and pepper.

2 Heat ½ Tbsp oil in a skillet on medium. Add onion and sauté until tender, 5 to 7 min. Add chickpeas, apple, raisins, and curry powder. Cook 3 min. Stir in remaining Tbsp flour and cook 30 seconds. Stir in remaining ¾ cup of milk. Cook until thickened, 2 to 5 min.

3 Lightly coat 10-in. nonstick skillet with oil and heat on medium. Add about ¼ cup batter, swirling to evenly cover skillet and cook until edges are set, 1 min. Flip and cook 30 sec.; transfer to a plate and cover to keep warm. Repeat for remaining crepes. Cover to keep warm.

4 Add spinach and ¼ tsp salt to chickpea mixture and cook just until wilted, about 2 min. Divide among crepes, fold each in half, and serve with lemon wedges.

ROAST CHICKEN SALAD WITH BUTTERNUT SQUASH AND FARRO

Every part of this satisfying salad boasts anti-inflammatory benefits, whether it's the protein-packed shredded chicken, the whole-grain farro, the colorful veggies and fruit, or the sweet olive oil vinaigrette.

ACTIVE 40 MIN.   TOTAL 40 MIN.   SERVES 4

1 cup farro

¼ cup extra virgin olive oil

¼ cup orange juice

2 tsp minced fresh ginger

½ tsp ground cumin

¼ tsp salt

¼ tsp pepper

2 cups roughly torn rotisserie chicken (bones and skin removed)

2 medium parsnips, peeled and shaved

3 cups peeled and thinly shaved butternut squash

1 cup red seedless grapes, halved

⅓ cup chopped flat-leaf parsley

¼ cup toasted pepitas

3 oz soft goat cheese, crumbled

PER SERVING: 604 cal, 32 g pro, 61 g carb, 9.5 g fiber, 15 g sugars (0 g added sugars), 28 g fat (7 g sat fat), 178 mg chol, 294 mg sodium

1 In a medium pot place the farro and 3 cups of water. Bring to a boil, reduce to a simmer, and cook until tender, about 25 min. Drain and cool.

2 In a large bowl, whisk together the olive oil, OJ, ginger, cumin, salt, and pepper.

3 Add the farro, torn chicken, parsnips, squash, grapes, and parsley to the bowl; toss everything to coat with the dressing. Top with pepitas and goat cheese and serve.

CHICKEN AND BLUEBERRY CHIMICHURRI SKEWERS

Load up on lean protein and brimming-with-antioxidants blueberries for a feel-good lunch that satisfies.

ACTIVE 40 MIN.   **TOTAL 40 MIN.**   **SERVES 4**

CHIMICHURRI

- ¼ cup red wine vinegar
- ¼ cup finely chopped flat-leaf parsley
- 3 Tbsp olive oil
- ½ small shallot, finely chopped
- 2 Tbsp finely chopped cilantro
- 1 Tbsp finely chopped oregano
- 2 cloves garlic, finely chopped
     Kosher salt
     Crushed red pepper flakes

SKEWERS & SALAD

- ½ lb grilled chicken breast, cut into pieces
- 6 oz blueberries
- 2 scallions, green parts only, cut into 1½-in. pieces
- 2 cups cooked quinoa (½ cup uncooked)
- 4 cups baby arugula

PER SERVING: 340 cal, 23 g pro, 29 g carb, 4 g fiber, 6 g sugars (0 g added sugars), 14.5 g fat (2.5 g sat fat), 48 mg chol, 180 mg sodium

1. **Make chimichurri:** In a jar, place vinegar, parsley, oil, shallot, cilantro, oregano, garlic, and a pinch each of salt and red pepper flakes. Seal jar and shake to combine.

2. **Assemble skewers and salad:** Slide chicken, blueberries, and scallions onto 8 skewers, repeating in that order.

3. Toss quinoa and arugula with 2 Tbsp chimichurri; fold in remaining blueberries. Serve with skewers and drizzle with remaining chimichurri.

GRAIN BOWL WITH SAUTÉED SPINACH

Getting your fill of high-fiber whole grains is easy when you can transform leftover quinoa or brown rice into a tasty, veggie-filled bowl.

ACTIVE 10 MIN.   **TOTAL 10 MIN.**   **SERVES 2**

- 2   cups leftover cooked grains (such as farro, brown rice, or quinoa), warmed
- 1   Tbsp olive oil
- 1   clove garlic, finely chopped
- 1   bunch spinach, thick stems discarded, leaves roughly chopped (about 4 cups)
     Kosher salt and pepper
- 1   medium tomato, cut into 1-in. pieces
- ½   avocado, diced
- 2   large eggs

PER SERVING: 458 cal, 14 g pro, 56 g carb, 9 g fiber, 2.5 g sugars (0 g added sugars), 21 g fat (4 g sat fat), 186 mg chol, 367 mg sodium

1 Divide grains between bowls. In a large nonstick skillet on medium, heat oil and garlic until garlic starts to turn golden brown, 1 min. Add spinach and ¼ tsp each salt and pepper and cook, tossing, until leaves begin to wilt, 1 to 2 min. Spoon on top of grains along with tomato and avocado.

2 In skillet on medium heat, cook eggs to desired doneness, 2 to 3 min. for runny yolks. Serve on top of grain bowls.

SEARED TILAPIA WITH SPIRALIZED ZUCCHINI

Swapping white pasta for sweet, roasted "zoodles" makes it easy to cut back on refined carbs and up your veggie intake at the same time.

ACTIVE 25 MIN.   TOTAL 25 MIN.   SERVES 4

1½ lbs zucchini
3 Tbsp olive oil, divided
   Kosher salt and pepper
4 small tilapia fillets (1½ lbs)
1 lemon, thinly sliced and seeded
2 cloves garlic, thinly sliced
1 Tbsp capers
½ cup fresh flat-leaf parsley, chopped

PER SERVING: 292 cal, 37 g pro, 8 g carb, 2 g fiber, 4 g sugars (0 g added sugars), 13.5 g fat (2.5 g sat fat), 85 mg chol, 399 mg sodium

1. Heat oven to 475°F. Line large rimmed baking sheet with reusable baking mat or parchment paper. Using spiralizer, spiralize zucchini, or slice zucchini into thin ribbons.

2. On prepared baking sheet, toss zucchini with 1 Tbsp oil and ¼ tsp each salt and pepper. Roast 15 min. Increase heat to broil and continue to cook until golden brown, 3 to 4 min.

3. Meanwhile, in large cast-iron skillet on medium-high, heat 1 Tbsp oil. Season fish with ¼ tsp each salt and pepper and cook until just opaque throughout, 2 to 3 min. per side. Transfer to plates.

4. Add remaining Tbsp oil to skillet along with lemon, garlic, and capers and cook, stirring occasionally, until garlic is golden brown and tender. Toss with parsley, then spoon over tilapia and serve with zucchini.

QUICK SEAFOOD STEW

You might not know it, but mussels are rich in anti-inflammatory omega-3 fatty acids. This broth packs an antioxidant punch too, thanks to lycopene-loaded tomatoes.

ACTIVE 25 MIN. TOTAL 25 MIN. SERVES 4

2 Tbsp olive oil
1 bulb fennel, quartered, cored, and thinly sliced
¼ tsp red pepper flakes
   Kosher salt and pepper
4 cloves garlic, grated
1 cup dry white wine
1 14-oz can crushed tomatoes
2 cups low-sodium seafood or chicken broth
½ lb mussels, rinsed
½ lb peeled and deveined medium shrimp
8 oz cod, cut into 2-in. pieces
¼ cup fresh flat-leaf parsley, chopped
   Crusty bread, for serving

① In large pot on medium, heat oil. Add fennel, red pepper flakes, and ½ tsp each salt and pepper and cook, stirring occasionally, until tender, 5 to 6 min. Stir in garlic and cook 1 min.

② Add wine and simmer until reduced by half, 5 to 6 min. Stir in tomatoes and broth and return to a simmer.

③ Add mussels, shrimp, and cod and simmer until fish and shrimp are opaque throughout and mussels have opened, 3 to 4 min. Sprinkle with parsley and serve with crusty bread if desired.

PER SERVING: 267 cal, 28 g pro, 18 g carb, 4 g fiber, 7.5 g sugars (0 g added sugars), 10 g fat (1.5 g sat fat), 107 mg chol, 963 mg sodium

ORANGE CHICKEN AND BROCCOLI STIR-FRY

Veggie-packed stir-fries are go-tos for quick and easy anti-inflammatory dinners. This one has a sweet orange sauce reminiscent of your favorite takeout dish—with way less sugar.

ACTIVE 5 MIN.   TOTAL 20 MIN.   SERVES 2

¼ cup orange juice

1 Tbsp reduced-sodium soy sauce

1 Tbsp orange marmalade

1 tsp cornstarch

2 Tbsp canola oil

½ lb chicken tenders, trimmed and cut into 1-in. pieces

1 scallion, thinly sliced, whites and greens kept separate

1 large clove garlic, minced

1½ tsp minced fresh ginger

Pinch of crushed red pepper flakes

¼ cup reduced-sodium chicken broth

1 lb broccoli crowns, chopped into florets

½ red bell pepper, thinly sliced

1½ cups cooked brown rice

PER SERVING: 540 cal, 36 g pro, 60 g carb, 11 g fiber, 11 g sugars (19 g added sugars), 2 g fat (2 g sat fat), 83 mg chol, 475 mg sodium

1. In a small bowl, combine the OJ, soy sauce, marmalade, and cornstarch. Stir until blended. Set aside.

2. In a wok or large nonstick skillet, heat the oil over medium-high heat. Add the chicken and cook, stirring frequently, until cooked through, about 5 min. Add the scallion whites, garlic, ginger, and red pepper flakes and stir to combine. With a slotted spoon, remove chicken to a plate.

3. Reduce the heat to medium. Add the broth and broccoli to the wok. Cover and cook 2 min. Increase the heat to high and add bell pepper. Cook, stirring frequently, until the broth evaporates and the vegetables are crisp-tender, about 2 min. Stir the sauce and add to the wok along with the chicken. Cook, stirring constantly, until the sauce thickens, about 2 min. Serve over the rice and sprinkle with the scallion greens.

ALMOND-CRUSTED STRIPED BASS

Pulverized almonds are just as crisp and buttery as breadcrumbs. But they've got fiber, protein, and healthy fats instead of refined carbs and empty calories.

ACTIVE 25 MIN.   TOTAL 25 MIN.   SERVES 4

2 Tbsp olive oil, divided

4 5-oz boneless, skinless striped bass fillets

¼ bunch fresh cilantro

⅔ cup blanched slivered almonds, toasted and roughly chopped

1 medium shallot, finely chopped

2 tsp grated lime zest plus 1 Tbsp lime juice, plus lime wedges for serving

1¼ tsp smoked paprika

1 tsp ground cumin

½ tsp ground cinnamon

¼ tsp ground allspice

Kosher salt and pepper

6 cups mixed greens

4 small radishes, thinly sliced

PER SERVING: 339 cal, 31 g pro, 11 g carb, 5 g fiber, 3 g sugars (0 g added sugars), 20 g fat (2.5 g sat fat), 117 mg chol, 503 mg sodium

1. Heat oven to 375°F. Line rimmed baking sheet with parchment paper and brush with 1 tsp olive oil. Pat fillets dry with paper towels and lay on parchment.

2. From cilantro, finely chop stems to equal ⅓ cup and set aside ½ cup leaves for salad. In medium bowl, toss together cilantro stems, almonds, shallot, lime zest, smoked paprika, cumin, cinnamon, allspice, ½ tsp salt, and 2 tsp oil. Season fish with ¼ tsp each salt and pepper and divide almond mixture among fillets, spreading to coat surface of fish and pressing to adhere. Roast until fish is just opaque throughout, 10 to 14 min.

3. Meanwhile, in large bowl, combine lime juice with remaining Tbsp oil. Add greens, radishes, reserved cilantro leaves, and a pinch each of salt and pepper and toss to coat. Serve with lime wedges if desired.

BREAKFAST

SNACK

LUNCH

SNACK

DINNER

DESSERT

NOTES

_____

_____

_____

_____

_____

_____

WATER

◯ ◯ ◯ ◯ ◯ ◯ ◯ ◯

MOVEMENT/WORKOUT

◯ YES ◯ NO

ACTIVITY _____

_____

_____

DURATION _____

_____

_____

INTENSITY _____

_____

_____

SLEEP

BEDTIME LAST NIGHT _____

WAKE TIME THIS MORNING _____

SLEEP QUALITY _____

_____

MOOD ☹ 😐 🙂 😀

_____

_____

_____

_____

_____

BREAKFAST

SNACK

LUNCH

SNACK

DINNER

DESSERT

WATER

◯ ◯ ◯ ◯ ◯ ◯ ◯ ◯

MOVEMENT/WORKOUT

◯ YES   ◯ NO

ACTIVITY _____
_____
_____

DURATION _____
_____
_____

INTENSITY _____
_____
_____

SLEEP

BEDTIME LAST NIGHT _____

WAKE TIME THIS MORNING _____

SLEEP QUALITY _____
_____

MOOD ☹ 😐 🙂 😄

_____
_____
_____
_____
_____
_____

NOTES

_____
_____
_____
_____
_____
_____

BREAKFAST

SNACK

LUNCH

SNACK

DINNER

DESSERT

WATER

○ ○ ○ ○ ○ ○ ○ ○

MOVEMENT/WORKOUT

○ YES   ○ NO

ACTIVITY _____
_____
_____

DURATION _____
_____
_____

INTENSITY _____
_____
_____

SLEEP

BEDTIME LAST NIGHT _____

WAKE TIME THIS MORNING _____

SLEEP QUALITY _____
_____

MOOD ☹ 😐 🙂 😄
_____
_____
_____
_____
_____

NOTES
_____
_____
_____
_____
_____
_____

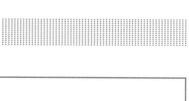

BREAKFAST

SNACK

LUNCH

SNACK

DINNER

DESSERT

NOTES

_____
_____
_____
_____
_____
_____

WATER

◯ ◯ ◯ ◯ ◯ ◯ ◯ ◯

MOVEMENT/WORKOUT

◯ YES   ◯ NO

ACTIVITY _____
_____
_____

DURATION _____
_____
_____

INTENSITY _____
_____
_____

SLEEP

BEDTIME LAST NIGHT _____

WAKE TIME THIS MORNING _____

SLEEP QUALITY _____
_____

MOOD   ☹ 😐 🙂 😀

_____
_____
_____
_____
_____
_____

BREAKFAST

SNACK

LUNCH

SNACK

DINNER

DESSERT

WATER

○ ○ ○ ○ ○ ○ ○ ○

MOVEMENT/WORKOUT

○ YES   ○ NO

ACTIVITY _____
_____
_____

DURATION _____
_____
_____

INTENSITY _____
_____
_____

SLEEP

BEDTIME LAST NIGHT _____

WAKE TIME THIS MORNING _____

SLEEP QUALITY _____
_____

MOOD ☹ 😐 🙂 😃
_____
_____
_____
_____
_____
_____

NOTES

_____
_____
_____
_____
_____
_____
_____

BREAKFAST

SNACK

LUNCH

SNACK

DINNER

DESSERT

NOTES

_____
_____
_____
_____
_____
_____

WATER

◯ ◯ ◯ ◯ ◯ ◯ ◯ ◯

MOVEMENT/WORKOUT

◯ YES   ◯ NO

ACTIVITY _____
_____
_____

DURATION _____
_____
_____

INTENSITY _____
_____
_____

SLEEP

BEDTIME LAST NIGHT _____

WAKE TIME THIS MORNING _____

SLEEP QUALITY _____
_____

MOOD ☹ 😐 🙂 😀

_____
_____
_____
_____
_____
_____

BREAKFAST

SNACK

LUNCH

SNACK

DINNER

DESSERT

WATER

◯ ◯ ◯ ◯ ◯ ◯ ◯ ◯

MOVEMENT/WORKOUT

◯ YES   ◯ NO

ACTIVITY _____

_____

_____

DURATION _____

_____

_____

INTENSITY _____

_____

_____

SLEEP

BEDTIME LAST NIGHT _____

WAKE TIME THIS MORNING _____

SLEEP QUALITY _____

_____

MOOD ☹ 😐 🙂 😄

_____

_____

_____

_____

_____

NOTES

_____

_____

_____

_____

_____

_____

BREAKFAST

SNACK

LUNCH

SNACK

DINNER

DESSERT

NOTES

_____
_____
_____
_____
_____
_____

WATER

○ ○ ○ ○ ○ ○ ○ ○

MOVEMENT/WORKOUT

○ YES   ○ NO

ACTIVITY _____
_____
_____

DURATION _____
_____
_____

INTENSITY _____
_____
_____

SLEEP

BEDTIME LAST NIGHT _____

WAKE TIME THIS MORNING _____

SLEEP QUALITY _____
_____

MOOD ☹ 😐 🙂 😄

_____
_____
_____
_____
_____
_____

PHOTO CREDITS

COVER PHOTOGRAPHY

Front: Con Poulos (tacos), Christopher Testani (slaw and bowl)

Back: Con Poulos (soup), John Kernick (waffles)

INTERIOR PHOTOGRAPHY

Armando Rafael: 155; Beatriz da Costa/Studio D: 119; Bob Martus: 153; Bobbi Lin: 76; Chelsea Kyle: 87; Chris Court: 159; Christopher Testani: 113, 115, 139; Con Poulos: 85, 93, 111, 125, 36; Danielle Daly: 75, 83, 97, 99, 100, 103, 141; Erika LaPresto: 95; Jason Varney: 78; John Kernick: 149; Mike Garten: 8, 12, 16, 34, 79, 80, 81, 89, 101, 105, 107, 117, 127, 129, 131, 135, 145, 146, 157, 161; Mitch Mandel: 91, 137, 143, 163; Paola + Murray: 165; Philip Ficks: 51; Philip Friedman: 109; Ruth Black: 21; Sarah Anne Ward: 96, 122; Susan Pittard/Studio D: 147

Adobe Stock: Anna Puzatykh: 15, 20 (water droplets); Aliaksandr: 33; baibaz: 35, deagreez: 32; janong054: 20 (beans); Kittiphan: 19; LIGHTFIELD STUDIOS: 13; mykolastock: 22; New Africa: 73; Okea: 17; Sunny Forest: 14; svetlana_cherruty: 18; tatomm: 31; vectorfusionart: 10; Tim UR: 174

Getty Images: Arx0nt: 25; Enrique Diaz/7cero: 24; iStockphoto/Farion_O: 20 (vitamins); iStockphoto/fcafotodigital: 20 (turmeric); iStockphoto/lithiumcloud: 30; LdF: 6; OlgaLepeshkina/iStock/Getty Images Plus: 121; Science Photo Library RF: 29; LILECHKA75/Getty Images: 133; Great Stock!/StockFood: 120; vicuschka/iStock/Getty Images Plus: 77

...22 by Hearst Magazines, Inc.

...ention is a registered trademark of Hearst Magazines, Inc.

...design by Gillian MacLeod and Karina Ponce

...pes by Kristina Kurek, Jennifer Kushnier, Sarah Mirkin, Julissa
...erts, Men's Health Test Kitchen, Prevention Test Kitchen,
...nan's Day Test Kitchen

...ary of Congress Cataloging-in-Publication Data is on file with
...publisher.

...J 978-1-955710-14-5

...ted in China

...10 9 7 5 hardcover

EARST